GROWING CATTLE MANAGEMENT AND DISEASE NOTES

PART 1 - MANAGEMENT

A.H. Andrews, BVetMed PhD MRCVS

(Presently Dr Andrews is Senior Lecturer, Department of Medicine, Royal Veterinary College.)

First Edition 1985

ISBN 0 9508820 1 1 Growing Cattle Management and Disease Notes
Part I - Management

ISBN 0 9508820 3 8 Growing Cattle Management and Disease Notes
Parts I and II - Management and Disease

Printed in Great Britain by: Centre Graphics Ltd, 12 Summer Walk, Markyate, Hertfordshire AL3 8NF.

Published by: A.H. Andrews, ~~11 Aran Close, Harpenden, Hertfordshire~~, ~~AL5 1SW~~

FOREWORD

Following the production of my book "Calf Management and Disease Notes" it is now logical to turn my attention to the next stage in the development of cattle. The period dealt with in the calf book was from birth to three months old. In this next study we observe the animals from about the three-month stage until they are slaughtered for beef or are entering the dairy or suckler herd as downcalving heifers.

Unlike the calf stage, this next period includes the potential for a large number of different management systems as well as disease conditions. Thus, for ease of use, it has been necessary to divide this second book into two volumes, the first concerned with management but also hopefully indicating some of the nutritional, genetic and disease considerations. The second part deals with the diseases and other conditions which can affect these growing cattle. It is intended that the two halves of the book should be used together, and they complement each other.

There are already several excellent booklets dealing with various management systems and produced by the Ministry of Agriculture, Fisheries and Food, Meat and Livestock Commission and Milk Marketing Board. There is also an excellent book on beef production, namely:-

ALLEN, D. and KILKENNY, B. (1984) "Planned Beef Production" 2nd edition, Granada Technical Books, London.

The two parts of this book do not in any way compete with the above as they tend to deal equally with management and disease.

I must thank the Meat and Livestock Commission and the Ministry of Agriculture, Fisheries and Food for permission to quote from their literature. The Ministry publications:-

MINISTRY OF AGRICULTURE, FISHERIES AND FOOD (1977) Straw as a Feeding Stuff. Leaflet 551, M.A.F.F., Pinner. pp. 1-7.

MINISTRY OF AGRICULTURE, FISHERIES AND FOOD (1982a) Grass Silage: Quality and Feeding. Leaflet 494, M.A.F.F., Alnwick. pp. 1-11.

MINISTRY OF AGRICULTURE, FISHERIES AND FOOD (1982b) Grazing Management for Beef Cattle. Grassland Practice No. 11. Booklet 2051. M.A.F.F., Alnwick. pp. 1-16.

MINISTRY OF AGRICULTURE, FISHERIES AND FOOD (1983a) Agricultural Statistics. Press Notice No. 236. M.A.F.F., London.

MINISTRY OF AGRICULTURE, FISHERIES AND FOOD (1983b) Silage Effluent. Waste Management Booklet 2429. M.A.F.F., Alnwick. pp. 1-10.

MINISTRY OF AGRICULTURE, FISHERIES AND FOOD (1983c) Rearing Spring-Born Friesian Dairy Heifers to Calve at 2½ Years. Booklet 2422. M.A.F.F., Alnwick. pp. 1-23.

MINISTRY OF AGRICULTURE, FISHERIES AND FOOD/DEPARTMENT OF AGRICULTURE AND FISHERIES FOR SCOTLAND/WELSH OFFICE AGRICULTURAL DEPARTMENT (1983) Codes of Recommendations for the Welfare of Livestock. Cattle. Leaflet 701. M.A.F.F., Alnwick. pp. 1-16.

It is hoped that this present book will be of use to veterinary students and practitioners. Although many technical words are used, I would hope that the two parts will have some relevance to farmers, stockmen and agricultural advisers. As information changes so rapidly, in many parts of the book spaces have been left to allow notes to be added by the reader.

Any work such as this is bound to contain some mistakes and to become slightly out-of-date. The author would be very pleased to hear of omissions, mistakes or to receive other comments. He would like to thank Mr D. Gunn for producing the figure on grass growth, and Mrs Rosemary Forster for once again undertaking the impossible task of deciphering my writing and translating it into type.

DR A H ANDREWS
25 MARDLEY HILL
WELWYN
HERTS AL6 0TT
Tel: WELWYN (043871) 7900

November, 1984

CONTENTS

CHAPTER 1

THE CATTLE INDUSTRY

Cattle Population

There are usually between 11 and 12 million cattle in Great Britain at the present time and this rises to over 13 million when Northern Ireland figures are included. Just over a third of this number are cows and these consist of approximately two-thirds dairy cows and one-third beef cows. Heifers amount to six per cent of total cattle and there is about one heifer to every 4 to 5 dairy cows and one to every 8.5 beef cows. This indicates the longer productive life of the beef animal but also shows a recent decline in the beef suckler herd population. Other cattle over two years old amount to about seven per cent of the total. They are relatively evenly divided into females and steers and most of the former will be put into calf, while most of the latter will be animals in semi-intensive and extensive beef systems. Cattle between one and two years and below one year old each amount to a quarter of the population, with a bias towards heifers.

TABLE 1.1

Cattle Population (June 1983 Census)

United Kingdom

		No. 000's	No. 000's	Percentage of Total
Dairy cows		3,331		
Beef cows		1,358		
TOTAL COWS			4,689	35.2
Dairy heifers		686		
Beef heifers		157		
TOTAL HEIFERS			843	6.3
Bulls		82.7		0.6
TOTAL ADULT			5,614.7	
TOTAL ADULT DAIRY			4,047	
TOTAL ADULT BEEF			1,567.7	
Over 2 years old	- Male	488		
	- Female	413	901	6.8
1 - 2 years old	- Male	1,246		
	- Female	1,829	3,075	23.1
6 mths - 1 year old	- Male	913		
	- Female	1,016	1,929	14.5
Under 6 mths	- Male	864		
	- Female	902	1,766	13.2
Slaughter calves		45.3	45.3	0.3
TOTAL YOUNG STOCK			7,716.3	
TOTAL CATTLE			13,331	100

(Source; M.A.F.F., 1983a)

Beef Production

The majority of beef produced in Britain is from the dairy herd. Table 1.2 shows that only about a third of beef comes directly from the suckler herd whereas all but six per cent of the remainder (Irish stores) is from the dairy herd. Looking at those cattle sold for beef, only about half comes from steers whereas a quarter arises from heifers and a further quarter occurs mainly from culled adult animals (Tables 1.2, 1.4).

The United Kingdom is not self-sufficient in beef and veal but it does export as well as import meat. Thus about 8 to 10 per cent of production is exported, but we import three times this amount by weight. When live cattle imports/exports are looked at, the balance on a headage basis is in favour of Britain with most cattle going abroad for slaughter. This is, however, greatly exceeded by the number of calves being exported to the Continent for further raising as veal. Imported cattle again mainly consist of animals for beef production rather than breeding (see Tables 1.5, 1.6, 1.7).

In this book, for simplicity's sake, intensive beef is defined as animals going to slaughter at around one year of age. Semi-intensive beef forms the bulk of British beef production (Table 1.3) and these are animals slaughtered from about 15 months to three years old. Extensive beef can be considered to include animals reared especially for beef and killed after the age of three years. This system involves only a small proportion of the total beef cattle produced.

TABLE 1.2

Sources of Beef Production

			Total
Dairy herd	- Cull cows	18%	
	- Calves - purebred	18%	
	- crossbred	25%	61%
Beef (suckler) herd	- Cull cows	5%	
	- Calves	29%	34%
Irish stores (feeder cattle)		6%	6%

(After Southgate, J. 1982)

TABLE 1.3

Age of Beef Production Animals at Slaughter

Under 12 months old	6%
Over 1 year, under 2 years	49%
Over 2 years	45%

(Source: Meat and Livestock Commission)

TABLE 1.4

Cattle Slaughterings

Steers	50%
Heifers	25%
Cows and Bulls	25%
	100%

TABLE 1.5

Beef and Veal Production

000's tonnes

United Kingdom	1977	1978	1982
Production	1001.5	1027.2	965
Exports	87.7	94.6	117.9
Imports:			
Beef - boneless	120.1	113.8	128.4
Beef - bone in	133.5	154.6	80.5
Veal	4.1	4.8	4.2
TOTAL	257.7	273.2	213.1

(Meat and Livestock Commission, 1979; 1983)

TABLE 1.6

Cattle Slaughterings, Imports, Exports in the United Kingdom

	000's Head		
Slaughterings	1977	1978	1982
Steers and heifers	2901	3003	2652
Cows and bulls	947	879	101
Calves	264	157	786
TOTAL	4112	4039	3539
Exports			
Cattle for breeding	18.4	18.2	
Other cattle except calves	98.0	82.6	
Calves	394.8	420.7	234
TOTAL	511.2	521.5	
Imports			
Breeding	0.3	0.8	
Others	304.0	352.7	
TOTAL	304.3	353.5	

(Meat and Livestock Commission, 1979; 1983)

TABLE 1.7

Percentage by Weight of Meat Produced from Different Types of Cattle in the E.E.C.

	Percentage				
	Cows	Heifers	Bulls	Steers	Veal and Bobby Calves
Belgium/Luxembourg	32	20	30	6	12
Denmark	42	10	46	1	1
Eire	24	26	1	49	<1
France	36	13	14	19	18
Italy	16	7	62	1	14
Netherlands	43	7	13	1	31
West Germany	30	12	52	2	4
United Kingdom	21	23	3	53	<1

(Allen and Kilkenny, 1984)

Castration

All but about five per cent of male calves destined for beef production are castrated. The exceptions are mainly reared in intensive or cereal beef systems. The reason for castration being so commonly undertaken in male cattle used for beef production is hard to comprehend completely. Obviously, castrated animals are easier to handle and do not cause problems for walkers or ramblers passing through the fields where they graze. This would have been doubly important in the past when animals were more extensively managed and so they would have been over three years old at the time of slaughter, and thus very mature. However, in many continental countries, castration is rather the exception than the rule. It is also possible that those countries with large suckler herd populations do tend to undertake more castration, and such a situation is also seen in the United States of America. Obviously, castration helps reduce management problems in suckler herds but pedigree herds do successfully manage bulls. Other factors have had an indirect influence. Thus the keeping of bulls for beef requires compliance with the Code of Practice for such beef production. In the past, subsidies were only paid for bulls at time of slaughter, whereas owners of steers of beef type could gain their subsidies at any age over eight months old.

Castration

A discussion on methods of castration has already been made in "Calf Management and Disease Notes". It must be remembered that all castration of bulls over two months old requires an anaesthetic (Protection of Animals (Anaesthetics) Act 1964) (Amendment Order 1982) and must be undertaken by a veterinary surgeon (Veterinary Surgeons Act 1966) (Amendment Order 1982). Both surgical castration with a scalpel or the bloodless method using a Burdizzo are commonly used. Where cattle are castrated by application of a rubber ring using an elastrator, this must be undertaken within the first week of life (Protection of Animals (Anaesthetics) Act 1964).

Many people consider that castration is an unnecessary mutilation and it could one day become a welfare issue. This is particularly so as it has little benefit in food production other than perhaps for helping the management of the animals. This has led to the study of other methods of cattle castration. Experimentally, it is possible to immunise a calf against its own luteinising hormone releasing hormone (LHRH) and thereby prevent the release of pituitary gonadotrophins from the pituitary. Injections of 2 mg synthetic LHRH were used on four occasions to maintain antibody levels (Robertson, Wilson and Fraser, 1979). This results in reduced testicular size, lowered testosterone secretion and reduced numbers of spermatozoa, with the animals being docile and steer-like (Robertson, Wilson, Rowland and Fraser, 1981). The duration of the suppressed response is variable but varied between 15 and 35 weeks, so that it would mean routine booster immunisations would be required to maintain the effect.

Economics

Various methods of presenting financial information are available. Particularly in beef production, the conventional method has involved calculating the gross margin and net profit. All the money received from sale of animals and their products equals the total returns (Table 1.8) of the enterprise. Gross output is then calculated by deducting from the gross returns the cost of the animal, cost of mortality or cost of replacements in terms of suckler or dairy herds, whichever is appropriate. The direct inputs into any system of production make up the variable costs and when these are subtracted from the gross output, the gross margin is derived. It must be emphasised that gross margin is not profit. This is the sum of money available to meet the fixed costs of the farm and the net profit. Those costs associated with running and operating the farm but which cannot be directly related to the particular enterprise being costed are the fixed costs. Deduction of these fixed costs from the gross margin produces the net profit which is the final method of judging the viability of a particular production system on a farm. When talking with farmers, the term 'working capital' is often mentioned. This can best be calculated as the cost of the animals concerned, plus half the variable costs.

Looking at the various systems of beef production mentioned in this book, no financial costs have been given, but they have been shown as a proportion of the gross returns on the enterprise. Generally, the longer the cattle are kept, the higher the gross returns and usually the gross margin is also greater. However, the working capital is also invested for a long period before any financial return is obtained. However, systems of a short-term nature tend to provide very wide fluctuations in gross margin. This is often seen in the purchase and selling of store or suckler cattle and depends on the price at purchase, which can fluctuate markedly from season to season, as well as in each season. Success in such enterprises depends on the prudent purchase and subsequent successful marketing of the animals.

TABLE 1.8

Conventional Financial Framework

Gross Output	=	Total Returns (price obtained for animal, price obtained for culls, any subsidies or premiums)	-	Stock Purchase (price of calf + mortality or cost of herd replacements)
Gross Margin	=	Gross Output	-	Variable Costs
Net Profit	=	Variable Costs	-	Fixed Costs
Variable Costs	=	Direct inputs to the system, e.g. Concentrate costs Forage costs (including fertiliser + conservation) Veterinary and medicine costs Market costs Transport costs Bedding Miscellaneous costs (AI, electricity, water, etc)		
Fixed Costs	=	Costs involved in running the farm which are not directly altered by the enterprise undertaken e.g. Labour Building depreciation Machinery depreciation Rent Rates (unlikely unless defined as an intensive farm) Repairs General overheads.		

References

ALLEN, D and KILKENNY, B (1984) Planned Beef Production. 2nd edition. Granada Technical Books, London. p.12.

MEAT AND LIVESTOCK COMMISSION (1979) UK Meat and Livestock Statistics. Meat and Livestock Commission, Bletchley.

MEAT AND LIVESTOCK COMMISSION (1983) Beef Yearbook. Meat and Livestock Commission, Bletchley. pp. 1-106.

MINISTRY OF AGRICULTURE, FISHERIES AND FOOD (1983a) Agricultural Statistics Press Notice, No. 236.

ROBERTSON, I S, WILSON, J C and FRASER, H M (1979) Veterinary Record, 105, 556-557.

ROBERTSON, I S, WILSON, J C, ROWLAND, A C and FRASER, H M (1981) Veterinary Record, 108, 381-382.

SOUTHGATE, J (1982) British Friesian Journal. May edition, 64, No. 3, pp. 218-219.

CHAPTER 2

GROWTH OF CATTLE

The growth of cattle is affected by various factors. When cattle develop, certain tissues have priority over others. In addition, growth is influenced by hybrid vigour, compensatory gain and maturity. Inheritance can also influence the growth rate of an animal. This Chapter deals simplistically with the concepts.

When farmers are producing cattle, particularly for beef, they often consciously or subconsciously make decisions which influence the likely end result of production. Thus they tend to buy colour-marked calves, i.e. white-faced animals (Hereford crosses) or light-coated cattle (Charolais crosses) because they know that although they are derived from dairy herds, they do contain some beef blood.

Sequence of Growth

When animals are growing, nutrients are allocated to different tissues according to a series of priorities. The sequence of importance is:-

First priority: brain, central nervous system, digestive tract;
Then : bone,
muscle,
fat.

Thus if nutrition is reduced, fat is the first tissue to stop being formed but as the deprivation becomes more severe, then muscle is also affected, and so on.

At one time the condition of sequential growth was explained by the idea that the body proportions changed due to different rates of growth. Thus there was a primary wave extending from the cranium to the facial part of the head and then to the lumbar region. There was a second wave of growth starting in the distal parts of the limbs and then extending to the ventral part of the trunk before ending in the lumbar region. This theory is probably wrong and has been superseded by the idea that the more expensive parts of the beef animal, i.e. the upper parts of the hind limbs, develop at a relatively slow rate of 90 per cent when compared with total muscle growth. Muscles around the spinal column grow at the same rate as total muscle whereas those of the abdomen develop last. As the animal grows, so fat deposition tends to increase. This overall increase in fat deposition occurs with approaching maturity of the animal and proportionally the expensive muscles tend to decrease and the less desirable muscles increase relative to the total muscle mass.

Hybrid Vigour

This has several other names, including heterosis and luxuriance. The definition of hybrid vigour is that when two breeds are crossed, the first generation performs at least midway between the parents. In general terms, the degree of heterosis is inversely proportional to the degree of heritability of a characteristic. Thus the less inherited a characteristic is, the more it tends to be enhanced. Thus improvements in reproductive efficiency are more affected than weight gain.

Hybrid vigour tends to be used in beef production for several purposes:-

1. Cross-bred cattle are used in the suckler herd.

    This produces: earlier puberty
    improved fertility
    improved calf survival.

2. Cross-bred calves are often produced for beef production.

    This is because of: improved survival once born
    reduced embryonic mortality
    improved birthweight
    improved pre-weaning weight
    improved weaning weight.

3. Cross-bred calves are often bought for beef production.

    This produces: a better daily liveweight gain
    a better weight for age.

Compensatory Gain or Growth

This condition occurs to some extent in all species of animals and birds. When the animal is subjected to factors which result in a lower growth rate than its potential, above average growth occurs once the depressing factor is removed. Making use of this fact can make an animal grow faster than one of comparable age fed continuously on a good diet. The usual retarding factors are poor nutrition and disease. The result of removal of the depressant factor is increased feed conversion efficiency.

Some of the increased weight gain is due to increased gut fill but it has been shown that cattle also put down tissue at a faster rate. Explanation of the phenomenon is not entirely satisfactory but theories have included the suggestion that presence of fat reduces the capacity of the digestive tract, or that the occurrence of fat reduces the capacity of the animal to remove volatile fatty acids from the blood.

Much work is at present being undertaken to see how best to regulate and utilise compensatory growth and gain to the best advantage. Several factors do seem to influence it.

1. The degree of undernutrition.

   Generally the more restricted the feeding of an animal is, the greater is the compensatory gain on the removal of the restriction.

2. Type of realimentation diet.

   The animals make better compensatory gain the higher the metabolisable energy of the new diet. Sufficient protein is also necessary in the feed.

3. Type of undernutrition.

   If the depression in weight gain by the diet only prevents the deposition of fat then the animal gains well. The same happens if depression includes a reduction in muscle formation. However, if the animal becomes stunted with depressed bone growth, then compensatory gain will not be so good.

Compensatory growth can be used in various ways.

1. When animals are restricted in their growth on a silage diet in the winter then compensatory gain occurs once the cattle go to pasture.

2. When buying stores it is better to buy slightly retarded cattle rather than those which have been overfed.

3. While high energy rations are necessary near slaughter to ensure adequate fat deposition and "finish", it is often best to include cheaper rations earlier on. Thus with cereal beef, using a diet with a lower energy content, e.g. maize silage or dried grass cubes, earlier on will allow full benefit to be obtained from the cereal later on.

4. When cattle are stored at grass they grow less towards the end of the grazing period. Thus when the animals are yarded for their finishing period they will exhibit compensatory gain.

Maturity

Cattle are selected for slaughter at a given degree of "finish" which is really a level of fat cover. Early-maturing cattle finish at a lighter weight than late-maturing animals. The characteristics of early and late maturity are in Table 2.1.

TABLE 2.1

Characteristics of Early and Late-Maturing Cattle

Early-Maturing	Late-Maturing
Slaughtered at an early age.	Slaughtered at a late age.
A quick turnover of animals.	The animals are heavy at slaughter so they produce a high gross return.
The cattle can be finished on a high forage diet.	Cattle cannot be finished on a high forage diet.
If cattle given much cereal then fat put on too early.	Cattle require cereals to finish.
The feed requirement is low.	The feed requirement is high.
Stocking rates can be high.	Stocking rates are low.
Animals are not suitable for intensive beef.	Animals suitable for intensive beef.
Animals suitable for grass finishing.	Animals not suitable for grass finishing.

Factors influencing maturity include:

Breed

Early-maturing - Aberdeen Angus, Murray Grey, Hereford, Galloway, Beef Shorthorn.

Late-maturing - Charolais, Holstein, Friesian, Simmental, South Devon.

Feed

Cereal diets reduce time to maturity.

Roughage diets increase time to maturity.

Sex

Heifers early-maturing.

Bulls late-maturing.

Hormones

Oestrogens reduce time to maturity for bulls and steers.

Genetics

The following is based on the writings of the late Ken Deeble (1981).

Inheritance of various characteristics allows genetic improvement in subsequent generations. The various traits can be enhanced by identifying male and female cattle which have a superior breeding value for a particular trait and then introducing them into the breeding system. There are two main types of trait:

QUALITATIVE, which involves only one or a few genes and the characteristics are such that animals can be easily divided into those with and those without the trait. In such cases expression of the trait in the next generation can easily be calculated by simple arithmetic. The traits include the characteristic of the polled gene as expressed in the Aberdeen Angus and Galloway and its dominance over the horned gene, and colour-marking of calves, e.g. the white face produced by the Hereford and the light coat colour produced by the Charolais.

QUANTITATIVE, which involves many genes. Usually the characteristics are expressed to a different degree in individual animals and again selection involves use of superior animals. Improved expression of the traits is more variable but can be calculated by statistical procedures. Most production characteristics fall within this group and include milk yield, butterfat levels, daily weight gain, etc.

An animal's phenotype, which is the appearance of the animal and its subsequent performance, is dependent on two factors.

(a) Its genotype (G) - which is the genes inherited from its parents. The genotype can be further subdivided into three, depending on the type of gene action involved.

   (i) Additive (A) The specific value or effect of each particular gene on a trait can be added up and this then will produce the 'Breeding Value' of the animal.

   (ii) Dominance (D) effects result where one of a pair of genes masks the effect of the other.

   (iii) Epistasis (I) effects, which are the result of an interaction between more than one pair of genes.

(b) All other factors including the environment (E) and management of the animal as well as its feeding and any disease it has suffered.

   There are also interactions between the genotype and its environment (G x E).

Thus the phenotype P = G + (E including G x E).

This phenotype can be expressed as:-

$$P = (A + D + I) + (E \text{ including } G \times E)$$

The additive effects are the traits which tend to be most stable and can be passed on from generation to generation and so tend to be synonymous with breeding value.

Heritability

The heritability (h^2) of a particular trait is expressed by the additive effects (A) as a proportion of the total performance (P).

Thus: $$h^2 = \frac{A}{P}$$

Calculations for heritability often vary widely and depend on the population used to work out the estimate. Heritability of a trait is the most important factor controlling the rate of genetic progress in that trait because it is the proportion of phenotype merit (P) which is passed on from parent to offspring. Thus it tends to control the progress and response in a breeding programme (see Table 2.2).

Breeding Programmes

These depend on two factors.

1. SELECTION - the ability to identify superior males and females for the one or more traits to be improved.

2. MATING SYSTEMS - Various systems can be used.
   (a) Mating animals which are related - in-breeding or line breeding.
   (b) Mating animals which are unrelated - crossbreeding or outcrossing within the breed.
   (c) Mating animals which appear phenotypically alike.
   (d) Mating animals which are phenotypically unlike each other.

Information used for Selection

Selection decisions are made on various pieces of information.

(a) The animal's pedigree.

(b) The record of the animal's own performance for required traits (this may include the results of a performance test).

(c) The record of its progeny or other relatives for the required traits (this may include the results of a progeny test).

(d) A combination of information from more than one of the above sources.

Obviously, recording information about the animal concerned gives the quickest results and is least costly to perform. However, information about progeny does usually provide much more accurate information about the breeding value of a particular animal. Obviously it is much longer before this information becomes available. It is also much more time-consuming and costly to amass. It is essential, when trying to define the breeding value of an animal which does not itself show the required characteristic, e.g. the merit of a bull for improving milk quality or quantity. Progeny recording or testing is of less value in growth traits which can be measured in the bull itself, e.g. daily liveweight gain, etc. However, even under these circumstances much of the production performance will depend on the environment and so any such measurement recording should be under controlled conditions, e.g. a performance test.

Selection Methods

Selection can be undertaken in three different ways.

(a) TANDEM METHOD. This involves concentration on one particular characteristic and selecting for it until it reaches an acceptable level. A second characteristic is then focussed upon, then a third, etc. This method works satisfactorily when the characteristics which are being concentrated upon are relatively independent. However, the system does not work well with most traits as they tend to be associated and so, as one concentrates on one characteristic, another tends to deteriorate.

(b) INDEPENDENT CULLING. This involves the culling of all animals which do not meet a certain level of performance. It can only be used effectively if one or two traits are concentrated upon, or the various traits being selected for are genetically associated.

(c) TOTAL SCORE OR INDEX. The animal is assessed on its total economic and genetic merit. This involves adding up both the genetic deficiencies in the individual as well as its merits, to produce an overall assessment value. This method of approach is at least as effective as independent culling or the tandem method.

Pathways of Genetic Improvement

There are four main pathways in which genetic improvement is transferred through a population. The breeding value of the next generation depends on the breeding values of the animals used in the four pathways. The four pathways are:-

(a) Bull sires, i.e. the bulls which will sire the next generation of bulls. These should obviously be the animals with the best breeding values. The proportion of improvement varies slightly according to the selection system used but in a typical dairy progeny test programme the improvement will be in the region of 45 per cent.

(b) Bull mothers, i.e. the cows which will be the mothers of the next generation of bulls. The proportion of improvement is about 35 per cent.

(c) Bulls which sire only cows in the next generation. The proportion of improvement is about 15 per cent.

(d) Cows which produce only the cows of the next generation. The proportion of improvement is about five per cent.

Genetic Progress

As the genetic make-up of an animal is fixed, progress depends on the substitution with superior animals. The response to selection (R) in each generation depends on:

(a) The heritability (h^2) of the trait(s).

(b) The Selection Differential (S) which is the average phenotype superiority of the animals selected as parents for the next generation compared with the group, herd or population from which these animals are selected.

(c) The Genetic Association or Correlation between the traits. This depends on how the genes which affect one trait influence another related trait. This influence can be advantageous, non-existent or antagonistic to progress. The effects of the association cannot be influenced but appropriate action can be taken to minimise or maximise their effects, depending on the desired outcome. Beneficial correlations exist between growth rate and feed conversion efficiency, and between milk yield and total milk solids yield. However, a slightly disadvantageous correlation exists between milk yield and fat percentage.

Thus basic genetic progress in a generation is dependent on:-

$$R = h^2 \times S \ (h^2 S)$$

However, the speed of genetic progress is dependent on how quickly each new generation is produced and so can express the given trait. This is Generation Interval (GI). By definition this is the average age in years of the parents when the progeny which will replace them are born. Thus there is a very short generation interval with chickens and, to a lesser extent, pigs. However, the interval in cattle tends to be long - even up to 12 years although in a dairy progeny testing programme it is about eight years.

The genetic progress per year is:-

$$R \text{ per year} = \frac{h^2 \times S}{GI(\text{in years})}$$

It is thus important for the farmer to reduce as far as possible his generation interval, as this will increase his ability to make genetic progress. Thus a farmer who is able to choose his genetic selection within a herd for 30 years will produce much more improvement if the generation interval is five years (six selection opportunities) than if the GI is 10 years (three selection opportunities).

Reference

DEEBLE, F.K. (1981) Principles of genetic improvement. British Cattle Veterinary Association Proceedings for 1980-81. British Cattle Veterinary Association, Macclesfield. p. 99-104.

TABLE 2.2

Approximate Heritabilities of Some Characteristics in Beef and Dairy Cattle

	Heritability (%)
Ratio of inter- to intra-muscular fat	80
Eye muscle area	70
Post-weaning growth rate	50
Final weight	50
Protein percentage (carcase)	45
Feed conversion efficiency	40
Subcutaneous fat thickness	40
Percentage fat in rib cut	40
Marbling of muscle	40
Birth weight	40
Conformation score	40
Fat percentage (carcase)	40
Muscle : bone ratio	30
Percentage first quality meat	30
Weaning weight	30
Milk yield	30
Milk fat yield	30
Milk protein yield	30
Calving interval	12
Calf survival	4

(Sources various: including Meat and Livestock Commission and Milk Marketing Board)

CHAPTER 3

FORAGE AND FEED ADDITIVES

Grassland Management

Most systems of rearing cattle depend to a large extent on the use of grass or conserved grass. The use of this valuable product has always been the cornerstone for ruminant nutrition. Grass growth tends to follow a pattern (Fig. 3.1) with a rapid rise in growth starting in March and reaching a maximum in May. There is then a decline in production until the beginning of July when a slight rise occurs, followed by a more gradual reduction in growth, which reaches negligible proportions by the end of October. The timing of the growth phases does alter, depending on the area of the country, although the same pattern is followed. Generally, grass growth is much greater in the spring than it is at mid-season. This causes problems as it means that with rearing animals, as they grow during the grazing season, so their appetite increases, and this is just the time when grass growth is decreasing. Thus, as the season goes on, stocking densities need to decrease. The early rapid grass growth means that there is surplus material which can ensure adequate conservation levels. These conserved areas can then be used for grazing and thereby decrease the stocking density. When cattle are being finished at grass, often the decline in growth coincides with the sale of some of the finished animals, and so again the stocking level is reduced.

TABLE 3.1

Time of Year and Relationship to Amount of Production

Time of Year	% of Production
mid-March - mid-June	49
mid-June - mid-August	28
mid-August - mid-October	23

Use of Fertiliser

There is a relationship between nitrogen fertiliser usage and grass growth. This growth can then be turned into the profitability of the enterprise. However, most farmers do not use sufficient fertiliser to maximise the growth response of grass. In addition, many farmers who do use fertiliser do not increase their stocking rates sufficiently to take maximum advantage of the greater production. The effect of use of fertiliser is modified by various factors (Meat and Livestock Commission, 1978), including:

Summer rainfall (the more rain, the greater the growth of grass).

The nutrient status of the soil (its nitrogen, phosphorus and potassium).

Nature of the soil (chalklands have poor grass growth, very heavy or very light soils produce little grass whereas medium to heavy soils produce most grass).

Slope and aspect (southerly-facing fields are best, moderate to free-draining fields; impeded or very free-draining fields produce less grass).

Height above sea level (usually the higher up the less grass produced. An altitude below 100 m (330 ft) produces most grass and that above 300 m (985 ft) produces least grass).

Soil depth (the deeper the soil, the better the grass growth).

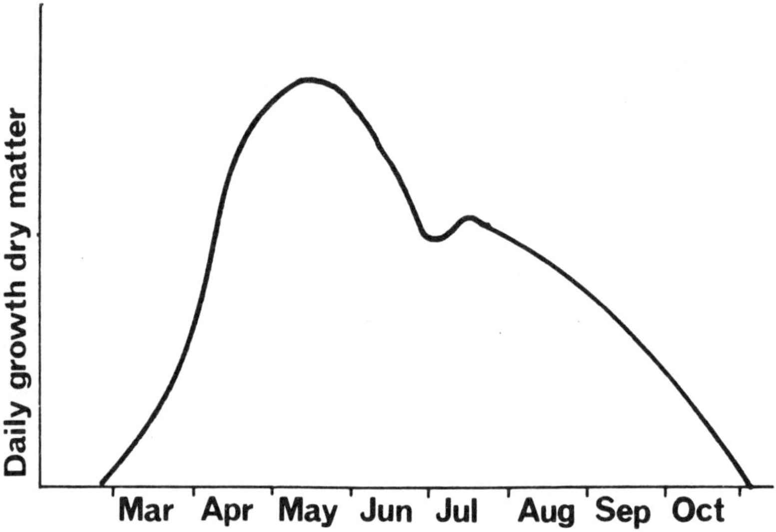

FIGURE 3.1

The seasonal pattern of grass growth in Great Britain

Although the response to fertiliser usage on a particular farm or field will vary according to the above factors, there is a consistent response with an almost linear increase in grass growth up to an annual application of 300 kg N per ha (265 lb per acre). In certain circumstances worthwhile increases in yield can be achieved by higher levels of 450 - 600 kg N per ha (395 - 530 lb per acre).

Phosphate and Potash Requirements

Increased use of nitrogen fertiliser enhances the requirements for other nutrients such as phosphate and potash. These elements should be added to the required amount following soil testing. The rate usually depends on soil type, and past cropping. Potassium levels are also affected by present management such as stocking rate and number of conservation cuts taken.

Phosphate: As a rule of thumb, usually about 30 kg phosphate per hectare (25 lb per acre) is useful for well-managed arable land. Neglected or poorly-managed land is more likely to require 60 kg phosphate per hectare (50 lb per acre).

Potash: The levels will vary according to the soil. Generally clay soils have sufficient potash whereas easily-drained soils containing little clay or organic matter are deficient. An annual level of 50 - 60 kg per hectare (40 - 50 lb per acre) is satisfactory for these light soils, provided it is applied in split applications. Conservation tends greatly to reduce potash levels and following a forage cut it is best to use 40 - 50 kg per hectare (35 - 40 lb per acre). In the spring, application of potash can lead to an increase in levels of hypomagnesaemia. It is thus best to dress fields in the autumn and omit dressing pasture in the spring if it is to be grazed. On other spring grass, a level of 20 - 30 kg per hectare (18 - 25 lb per acre) is satisfactory.

Farmyard Manure

This can be helpful in providing fertiliser to pastures. It is best applied in late winter or early spring when the grass is relatively short. When placed on very bare pastures there can be a delay in growth, probably because the growing shoots are smothered. However, cattle slurry will only provide about 30 *per cent* of the nitrogen requirement over the season. It is likely to give about 60 *per cent* of any phosphate requirements but it will probably overcompensate for any potassium loss. The high potassium level can exacerbate any problems of hypomagnesaemia. Problems of water pollution can also occur as surplus nitrogen may readily become nitrate and enter land drains and ground water. This can be overcome by long-term storage. Nutrients in farmyard manure or slurry are shown in Table 3.2.

Heavy farmyard manure levels without sufficient time being allowed to elapse prior to grazing can lead to rejection problems. Where application is uneven, areas with least slurry on them are preferred by the cattle. Where possible, the slurry should be used on grass for cutting. Direct injection of the slurry into the soil avoids herbage rejection and pasture wastage (Pain and Broom, 1978).

Farmyard slurry can result in disease problems and in particular, salmonellosis. This risk can be reduced by storing the slurry for a month before spreading. The use of rain guns or tankers which spread the slurry in the air can lead to the production of fine droplets, and these may help to spread infection, including foot-and-mouth disease virus.

Human Sludge

This has a relatively similar nutrient pattern to cattle slurry. It has problems with herbage acceptability by cattle when used. Disease can be present in the slurry including *Salmonella* spp. and cattle grazing such pastures have, on occasion, been found to be suffering from *Cysticercus bovis* at slaughter

Reference

PAIN, D.F. and BROOM, D.M. (1978) Animal Production, 26, 75-83.

TABLE 3.2

Available Nutrients in Undiluted Slurry and Farmyard Manure

	Nitrogen		Phosphate		Potash	
	kg/m³	lb/yd³	kg/m³	lb/yd³	kg/m³	lb/yd³
Slurry						
Cattle	2.5	4.2	1.0	1.6	4.5	7.5
Pigs	4.0	6.7	2.0	3.4	2.7	4.5
Poultry	9.0	15.1	5.5	9.3	5.5	9.3
	kg/ 10 tonnes	lb/ 10 tons	kg/ 10 tonnes	lb/ 10 tons	kg/ 10 tonnes	lb/ 10 tons
Farmyard Manure						
Cattle	15	34	20	45	40	89
Pigs	15	34	40	89	25	56
Poultry (deep-litter manure)	100	223	90	201	100	223
Poultry (broiler manure)	145	324	110	246	105	234

TABLE 3.3

Grass Production at Different Sites and Levels of Fertiliser Nitrogen

Type of Site	Clover	Nitrogen		Dry Matter Yields	
		kg/ha	lb/acre	tonnes/ha	tons/acre
Poor	No	150	130	5.3	2.1
	Yes	150	130	6.5	3.4
	No	300	265	7.7	3.1
Average	No	150	130	6.6	2.6
	Yes	150	130	8.0	3.2
	No	300	265	9.4	3.8
	No	450	405	10.7	4.3
Good	No	150	130	7.2	3.3
	Yes	150	130	9.0	3.6
	No	300	265	10.7	4.3
	No	450	405	12.2	4.9
Very Good	No	150	130	9.8	3.9
	Yes	150	130	10.8	4.3
	No	300	265	12.7	5.1
	No	450	405	14.3	5.7

(Meat and Livestock Commission, 1978)

The number of cattle which can be grazed on any particular area depends on the type of land, fertiliser application and whether or not clover is present. Generally, the better the land, the more nitrogen which is used or the more clover present, the higher the dry matter yield (Table 3.3) and therefore the greater the stocking rate. Usually cattle take in between 60 and 90 per cent of the available herbage. Provided the grass is consumed at intervals of three to five weeks it tends to maintain a D value of 70 and an energy value of 10.5 mJ/kg DM. The amount of grass consumed is dependent on stocking density and the severity of grazing. When the grass sward is short then the cattle have some difficulty in prehension. Problems tend to occur when the whole sward is below 7.5 cm (3") in spring and 9.5 cm (4") later in the grazing season. Because the grass has a sequence of growth, grassland management is essential. Thus in the early season, areas should be allocated for conservation. Following cutting the area can subsequently be used for grazing the cattle when grass production is slower. When grass is in short supply it can be supplemented with concentrates and conserved grass. Grassland management systems are dealt with under parasitic gastro-enteritis control (Growing Cattle Management and Disease Notes, Part II).

TABLE 3.4

Conserved Grass Production as Determined by Area Conserved and Time of Cutting

Conservation Area		Time of Conservation	Amount of Total Production Conserved
Half		May	30%
Two-Thirds	plus	May	45%
One-Third		July	

TABLE 3.5

Approximate Appetite and Stocking Rates for Growing Cattle at Grass

Liveweight										
kg	70	135	170	230	250	320	385	410	455	570
lb	155	300	375	505	550	705	845	900	1000	1255
Appetite - dry matter										
kg	2	3.7	4.6	6.3	7	8	9	9.5	10	12
lb	4.4	8	10	14	15	17.5	20	21	22	26

Stocking rate: Liveweight/Unit Area

	kg/ha	lb/acre
Turnout	2200	1950
Mid-Season	1650	1450
Housing	1150	1025

(Sources various; including M.A.F.F. Booklet 2051 (1982*b*))

Silage

Over 24 million ton(nes) of silage are made annually in the United Kingdom. Anaerobic fermentation of the grass produces silage. The chemical changes in anaerobic fermentation result in a change of sugars to organic acids, predominantly lactic acids and alcohols, and the protein is converted to amino-acids. The fermentation is by lactobacilli which work best in a slightly acid environment and produce lactic acid. Good fermentation depends on the presence of anaerobic conditions, the presence of enough sugar in the grass and a lack of contamination with other organisms.

Silage Making

Ensuring the best possible feed values of the silage depends first on the grass and then on when it is cut. A D value of 70 is seen with ryegrass cut in the second half of May in the south and at the end of May in the north. Once the flowering heads begin to emerge, the D value falls by two or three *per cent* each week, so that by mid-June the value is 58 - 65. Regrowth digestibility depends on the rate of regrowth. A four to five week regrowth in June to August would have a D value of 65 - 70 *per cent*, while a six to eight week growth in August to October produces a value of 60 to 65 *per cent* (M.A.F.F. 1982*a* - Leaflet No. 494). Harvesting of the crop should be as quick as possible to reduce risks from weather, to ensure cutting at the right stage and to reduce losses in the field and silo before the latter is finally sealed.

Systems

Direct Cutting

This is the most simple silage making system. The grass may be single- or double-chopped. The cut herbage is not wilted but is at once passed into the trailer. For 700 ton(nes), three men with three tractors can deal with 0.8 ha (2 acres) per hour. The machinery includes a single, or more probably double-chop forage harvester, two silage trailers and a buck rake. Double-chopped silage is consolidated more easily than single chop and requires less rolling. More cut grass can also be held in the trailer when it is chopped twice.

Double-Chopping with Wilting (Wilting- see page 38)

The grass is cut with a mower and turned with a windrower turner as for hay-making. A double-chop forage harvester can pick up the grass after cutting and wilting although it can also be used for the initial cutting. As the grass is double-chopped it consolidates better and requires less rolling. Also, the trailer can take a greater amount of grass per load. Again two silage trailers are required and for 700 ton(nes) three men with three tractors are required and can deal with 0.6 ha (1.5 acres) per hour.

Big Bale Silage

The grass is cut with a mower and wilted with a windrower turner. Baling occurs when there is a dry matter content of at least 25 *per cent*, using a big baler. The bales are sealed in plastic bags and these are carted to the stock for feeding. For 700 ton(nes) of silage, two men and tractors are required and they can deal with 0.5 ha (1.25 acres) per hour. Bales should be stacked in the gaps of the lower layer rather than one on top of the other.

Forage Wagon

The forage wagon can pick up and chop the grass. The grass is first cut with a mower and wilted by using a windrower turner before being picked up by the wagon and taken to the silo. For 700 ton(nes) grass, two men and tractors are required and can deal with 0.5 ha (1.25 acres) per hour.

Silage Storage

Field Clamp

This has no sides and is placed in a corner of a well-drained field. It is covered with polythene sheeting and weights applied (usually old tractor tyres). It can be fed direct to overwintered stock or cut and carried to housed stock.

Earth-Walled Clamp

A more permanent structure with the silo walls made of earth banks with the grass covered with polythene sheeting. The floor is often of concrete or if soil conditions permit, it can be hardcore. Pits can also be made by digging a pit in a field, with two approaches, or one if the field is on a hillside with the pig dug into it. The silo can be used for self-feeding or cutting and carrying.

Sleeper-Walled Clamp

This has a concrete base and can then be permanent. The sleepers should be covered with polythene fertiliser bags to cover splintered wood, etc. The whole pit should then be lined with polythene sheeting and the grass is also covered with sheeting. There is little maintenance but the stresses to which the walls will be put mean that the foundations must be firm enough and supports added. Where sleepers cannot be obtained there are proprietary brands of silo wall in wood or concrete.

Big Bale Silage Store

The bales can be stored on any level area which is free-draining and sheltered. The bags must not be punctured by sharp stones, etc. Thus the floor should be lined with polythene or sand. Vermin must be excluded from the area.

Silo Towers

These can be metal or concrete. They tend to be little used today because of the high costs.

TABLE 3.6

The Silage Quality and Cutting Date for Various N.I.A.B. Recommended Grass Varieties

		MAY				JUNE					
		10-15	15-20	20-25	25-31	1-5	5-10	10-15	15-20	20-25	25-30
Cocksfoot, early	S 37	66 →		63 →		<60					
Cocksfoot, late	S 26		66 →		63 →		<60				
Italian ryegrass	S 22				66 →		63 →		<60		
Meadow fescue, early	S 215			66 →		63 →		<60			
Perennial ryegrass, early	S 24			66 →		63 →		<60			
Perennial ryegrass, medium	S 101					66 →		63 →		<60	
Perennial ryegrass, late	S 23						66 →		63 →		<60
Timothy, early	S 352				66 →		63 →		<60		
Timothy, late	S 51					66 →		63 →		<60	

Silage Quality

All silage should be analysed so that its metabolisable energy and digestible crude protein are both known. Quality depends on the feeding value, the dry matter content, type of fermentation, the chop length, feeding method and protein level.

Feeding Value

This depends on the time when the grass is cut. The digestibility of grass declines as the season progresses and it is related to the proportion of leaf which is present. Thus it is high (about 70 per cent) in May when the crop is short and leafy and then long and leafy, but has reduced by June when some seed heads are formed. Digestibility then falls rapidly until mid-June when many seed heads are present. Cuts from silage aftermath that are leafy have a similar digestibility (65 per cent) to those of late May. If, however, grass is tall and stemmy, then digestibility is likely to be about 60 per cent, which is the same as for mid-June. The metabolisable energy level tends to fall parallel with the D value and so is over 12 mJ/kg DM when the grass is short and leafy but it is around 9 at the many seed head stage. The ME of a silage can be assessed by the amount of leaf present and the coarseness of the grass stems.

Fermentation

This must be anaerobic with the aim of producing large quantities of lactic acid. This is best achieved with a 20 to 30 per cent dry matter content. Wetter grass has less carbohydrate available to produce the lactic acid and in such cases butyric acid is more likely to be produced. Some of the problem can be offset by the use of silage additives. Those cuts with a high dry matter level must be well rolled. Problems can occur with overheating and mould development.

Well-fermented silage has only a slight, not unpleasant smell, which is acidic in nature. The silage tends to be readily identifiable into its various constituents and its colour is yellow, brown or green. A highly butyric silage has an unpleasant pungent smell. The constituents are shiny and easily disintegrate on handling. Overheated silage has a burnt smell to it and is dark brown or black in colour.

Dry Matter (DM)

As the dry matter level rises, so the amount of silage consumed by the cattle falls. However, on a weight basis more feed material is present and so there is a greater intake of nutrients by the animals. Dry matter content should be analysed prior to use of the silage. Once the clamp is opened, regular dry matter assessments should be made, particularly when the feed is being offered in troughs. When silage is squeezed and juice runs out, the dry matter level is less than 20 per cent. If only a few drops of juice can be squeezed out the DM is 25 to 26 per cent. If the palm of the hand is wet after squeezing and there are no drops of juice, the level is 26 to 30 per cent.

Chop Length

Shorter chopped silage tends to pack tighter and so fermentation is improved. This can result in a three per cent improvement in digestibility.

Silage Quantity

The value of silage = length (yd) x width (yd) x average depth (yd). This produces cubic yards which, multiplied by the density, gives the weight in wet matter. One cubic yard is about 10 cwt (½ ton) and so dividing by two or multiplying by 0.5 produces the weight in tons. The volume can also be calculated in cubic metres and one cubic metre of silage weighs about 0.66 tonnes.

Type of Feeding

Younger cattle will tend to eat more silage if it is in troughs than self-fed by silage clamp. Older cattle will eat roughly the same weight however the forage is fed.

Self-Fed

About 15 cm (6") width should be allowed for each young animal with 24-hour access. The height of the clamp should be no more than so that the silage can be easily pulled by the cattle, i.e. about 150 cm (5 ft) for young stock. About 15 cm (6") depth must be eaten daily, otherwise secondary fermentation may occur. Self-feeding saves labour and silage-handling equipment. However, there tends to be more wastage, the intake cannot be well controlled and sometimes there can be a considerable amount of slurry at the feeding face, if not well-drained.

Trough-Feeding

Silage should be fed at least once daily to prevent spoilage. Also cutting must not disturb the silage face and thereby allow secondary fermentation and moulding. The silage can be regulated this way but equipment and labour are required to cut and carry.

Feeding Big Bale Silage

Forage boxes and mixer wagons are unsuitable for feeding big bales. These are placed in ring feeders or rolled out behind a feed manger. A modified fore-end loader can be used. Some farmers use low trailers with sides of diagonal bars to make a hopper.

Protein Levels

The level of crude protein is between 10 - 25 <u>per cent</u> of the dry matter, but it varies depending on the grass species, fertiliser treatment and growth stage. Although during wilting the crude protein level remains relatively constant, with about 80 <u>per cent</u> as true protein, fermentation results in a breakdown of protein to non-protein nitrogen (NPN)e.g. amino-acids, amines and ammonia. In well-fermented silages only 40 <u>per cent</u> of the crude protein is in the form of true protein. Digestible crude protein (DCP) is little affected by fermentation and remains similar to that in grass at about 60 - 180 g/kg DM (0.6 - 1.8 <u>per cent</u>). Digestibility of the protein is, however, less because of the high levels of NPN. If fermentation temperatures become high and the silage overheats, protein digestibility can be markedly reduced.

Fermentation

Once oxygen is excluded from the silage clamp, the grass is digested by anaerobic bacteria which produce alcohols, carbon dioxide and mainly organic acids such as lactic and acetic.

If the grass fails to become sufficiently acid, secondary fermentation occurs with a reduction in lactic acid and an increase in butyric acid levels.

Non-Protein Nitrogen (NPN) Content

This includes amino-acids, amines, nitrates and ammonia. In the freshly-cut crop about 20 per cent of the crude protein is non-protein nitrogen. During wilting the amount of NPN increases but little ammonia is present. Once the grass enters the silo, protein breakdown occurs until stable acidic conditions are reached. Thus, at commencement of ensiling, there is a large and rapid breakdown of protein. In poorly-fermented butyric silages 20 to 30 per cent of the crude protein is in the form of ammonia.

The ammonia nitrogen (NH_3N) level is a good indication of fermentation quality. Thus a NH_3N level of less than 12 per cent of total nitrogen (N) is a sign of a well-preserved silage. Levels of 12 - 18 per cent indicate deterioration in the fermentation process and values above 18 per cent indicate poor preservation.

Digestibility (D value)

The aim is a level of 66. If the D value is high then the cattle will perform better and therefore they require less extra feed.

Wilting

The value of wilting has always been recommended to increase the dry matter content of the silage and to improve the fermentation process. It also speeds up silage making, has a shorter chop length and reduces the amount of effluent produced. The use of direct cutting of silage often means that a silage additive is necessary to ensure good fermentation. In addition, the extra silage effluent can be a considerable problem, particularly as water authorities are tending to penalise heavily any pollution of streams, etc. which occurs.

It thus seems that wilting should be undertaken, but the degree to which it is undertaken must be controlled. Prolonged wilting leads to a loss of carbohydrate with a lowering of both D and ME values. When silage is to be fermented in a clamp, the dry matter level should be between 25 and 30 per cent. Big bale silage should be wilted for 48 hours unless weather conditions are bad. Grass entering tower silos needs a high dry matter content of at least 35 per cent. In wet weather, wilting may not be possible and in such circumstances chemical additives will be necessary to ensure good quality silage. Otherwise it may be best to wait a few days until the weather improves and accept the decline in digestibility. Otherwise a large quantity of effluent loss will occur in cutting the wet grass. However, there does come a time when the grass must be cut before D values fall too low.

Silage Additives

About half of all silage made is treated with additives. Various types are available and they can be used in solid or liquid forms. Liquid additives increase the moisture content of the grass slightly.

Stimulants

Microbial stimulants are used to assist natural fermentation by the provision of extra carbohydrate, usually in the form of molasses. In some cases fermentation is stimulated by the direct inoculation of bacteria. The amount to be used is at least three *per cent* but must be evenly distributed.

Inhibitors

Microbial inhibitors reduce the bacterial activity in a crop by direct acidification and can thereby reduce nutritional losses. Many of the chemicals are acids or formaldehyde.

Formic Acid

The main use of formic acid is to help the preservation of silages which would otherwise be unlikely to conserve well. The additive results in improved silage digestibility, and increased silage intake.

Formaldehyde

This reduces microbial activity and helps to decrease the amount of protein breakdown within the rumen. However, if used at too high levels there is a reduction in protein digestibility and silage intake.

Silage Effluent

Considerable problems can arise for farmers from silage effluent. Farmers often receive heavy fines for polution of watercourses by effluent and civil actions can follow where fish etc. are killed. Discharge of effluent into any water supply is illegal without the written permission of the Water Authority. Such pollution is covered by The Rivers Prevention of Pollution Acts 1951 and 1961, and Control of Pollution Act 1974 (M.A.F.F. 1983b;Silage Effluent. Farm Waste Management Booklet 2429). Silage effluent can be reduced by wilting the grass, and ensuring that silage clamps are adequately covered to prevent rain access. The effluent can be collected in tanks and spread on land or fed to pigs.

TABLE 3.7

Effluent Production from Ensiling Grass in a Clamp Silo

Grass Dry Matter	Total Effluent Produced	
%	Litres per Tonne	Gallons per Ton
15	150 - 330	33 - 73
20	60 - 220	13 - 50
25	10 - 110	2 - 25

(Source: M.A.F.F. 1983b)

Anaerobic Fermentation

It is essential that air is excluded as quickly as possible to prevent the breakdown of grass carbohydrates to acids other than lactic. In poorly-fermented silages a large amount of the amino-acid is further degraded to organic acids, amines, carbon dioxide and ammonia. This means that as the clamp is filled it should be rolled. Usually this is done by a weighted tractor with a buck rake. Additionally, the whole clamp must be covered by polythene sheeting at the end of the day's work. Filling the clamp should follow a Dorset wedge-shape pattern with the back of the clamp being filled first. Once filled, the clamp should be thoroughly sealed and weighed down, usually with old tyres, to stop air movement.

Contamination

Any form of contamination of the grass will reduce the amount of fermentation to lactic acid. Sources of other bacteria include soil, which arises from digging up the soil while grass cutting, molehills and the tractor wheels. Faeces can also be introduced by the tractor wheels, as well as perhaps being present on the silo floor if it has not been cleaned out properly or if an application of slurry has been applied too close to cutting. Another source of contamination is the presence of old silage on the walls or floor of the silo, again if not properly cleaned out.

Measuring Silage Intake

This involves measuring the volume consumed over a period of two or three weeks (cubic metres) and multiplying it by the density in kg/cu mm^3. The density of silage is not constant and depends on dry matter content, chop length and type. The density can be accurately measured when taking samples by a corer. Where this is not done, the silages with a dry matter content above 23 _per cent_ have a density of 170 kg/m^3 (490 lb/yd^3) and those below 23 _per cent_ dry matter have a density of 140 kg/m^3 (400 lb/yd^3).

Lucerne Silage

This is little used but in a good lucerne silage only 10 _per cent_ of the protein is present as ammonia although 50 _per cent_ will be in the form of amino-acids due to protein hydrolysis. This results in most of the protein being rumen degradable.

Hay Production

Hay has always been the traditional form of grass conservation. Over the last ten years, the percentage area cut for hay has been declining and that for silage increasing. Today a greater area is used for silage than hay, although hay production is still in the region of 5.5 million ton(nes).

Haymaking involves cutting the grass to provide a high digestibility feed. The hay has to be assisted in drying by laceration and turning until it is ready to bale. The aim is to eliminate moisture quickly until it reaches about 20 per cent so that losses due to fungi and other micro-organisms are minimal. Baling can usually take place in five days. However, the weather often makes good quality haymaking extremely difficult and this is why silage is continuing to gain favour.

TABLE 3.8

Analysis of Hay cut in Southern Britain at Different Times in June

Time of Cutting	Forage Analysis: Digestibility Value %	Metabolisable Energy mJ/kg DM	Crude Protein %	Dry Matter tonnes/ha	Dry Matter tons/acre
Early June	70	11.0	13.8	4.5	1.8
Mid-June	67	10.4	13.2	5.4	2.15
Late June	62	9.6	13.4	5.2	2.06

The best time to make hay is when ear emergence is no more than 20 to 50 per cent for early flowering varieties, i.e. it is similar to the correct time for silage production.

Hay Quality

Good quality hay depends on rapid and even field drying. This reduces nutritional losses due to respiration. Digestibility also depends on the type of grass used and the time of cutting. The later the first cut is made the less drying is required and the greater is the total dry matter yield, but the poorer is the digestibility. Poor quality is also due to growth of moulds and other fungi that cause spoilage during storage of the baled crop. Quality can be assessed by the feeding value, colour and smell. Looking at the hay, the greater the proportion of leaf and the fewer the number of flowering heads, the better is the quality of the hay.

Feeding Value

Quality is best assessed by the digestibility or D value and is shown in Table 3.9. Traditionally, hay tends to be cut with a full flowering head with a D value of 55 - 60 per cent (third quality).

Nutrient Loss

The value of the hay is never higher than the constituents present at cutting. Most losses are from the least fibrous parts of the plant and depend on the method of haymaking and the length of time taken to make it. Losses are large during field drying. Rain exposure also tends to increase losses. Best hay is made either when barn dried or quickly made field-cured hay under good weather conditions.

Colour

Good quality hay has a fresh green colour. Pale, bleached plants means over-exposure to the sun, and dark brown hay means over-drying. A dull grey-brown colour indicates high losses due to bad weathering.

Smell

Field-dried hay has a pleasant, wholesome smell, although barn dried hay has little odour. A burnt sugar smell occurs with overheating but this changes to a charred or tobacco type if severe problems have occurred. Mouldy hay obviously smells mouldy!

Heating

If hay is badly made, heating of bales may occur. This is due to rapid microbial multiplication which results in a loss of energy and protein, thereby reducing the feeding value of the hay. Growth of mould which occurs can result in farmer's lung in man, as well as abortion or bovine farmer's lung in cattle.

Quantity Fed

The quantity of hay fed depends on its quality. Traditional medium quality hay can be fed to appetite whereas very good hay should be rationed and care should be taken when feeding poor hay to animals where good growth is desired. Satisfactory weight gains can be obtained by adjusting the amount of concentrates fed to the quality of the hay.

TABLE 3.9

Feeding Value of Hay

Quality	D Values	
First	65 - 70%	Young, early, few flowering heads present.
Second	60 - 65%	Much leaf, many early stage flowering heads.
Third	55 - 60%	All flowering heads.
Fourth	< 55%	Mature fibrous stems, heads seeding with seeds shed.

Drying

The speed of drying is dependent on the degree and the type of mechanical treatment, the density of the swath and the weather. About three ton(nes) of water have to be removed for each ton(ne) of hay produced. The mechanical treatment lacerates and bruises the stems of the crop. The leaves tend to dry more quickly than the stems. The stems are thicker, and have fewer pores so bruising, abrading or flattening helps to improve the drying rate. Excessive laceration or chopping should be avoided as this results in losses at later stages of drying.

Swath density is important in that the crop can only dry quickly if air can circulate freely through the swath. If the mower does not leave the swath open, then it should be tedded immediately to allow maximum air movement. Initial treatment is important as three-quarters of the plant's water is lost during the first third of the drying period and moisture content reduces from 80 per cent to 50 per cent. Subsequent crop water loss usually consists of a reduction to 20 per cent but this loss only includes about one-fifth of the plant's total water content which is held within the plant's tissues. The reduction of moisture content from 50 to 20 per cent is increasingly difficult and takes the remaining two-thirds of the drying time. Turning the swath helps drying to be even. The use of a mower/conditioner is helpful. This has tines which abrade the crop as it leaves the drum mowing discs and produces a loose, open swath.

Weather factors affecting drying include ambient temperatures, radiation humidity, and wind speed. Rain also has to be avoided and the risk can be overcome by barn drying. If barn drying is not undertaken, the last difficult stage of drying depends on the sun, wind and time. At this stage tedding should be minimised because the leaves will have dried more quickly than the stems and so they are liable to be brittle and break.

Desiccant

Rapid drying of the crop can be achieved with the use of 30 per cent formic acid applied at mowing time. Although moisture is rapidly removed from the leaves with this method, drying of the stem is little affected and so baling time is little reduced.

Tedding

Frequent tedding often results in quicker drying than does the use of chemical desiccation.

TABLE 3.10

A Typical Sequence of Haymaking

Day	
Day One	Cut with mower/conditioner or finger-bar mower. Crimp and ted.
Day Two	Turn swath, ted twice.
Day Three	Turn swath, ted once.
Day Four	Turn swath, ted once.
Day Five	Turn swath, windrow and bale.

Barn Drying

Hay can be removed from fields at a moisture content of 30 - 40 per cent for conventional bales and 30 - 35 per cent for big bales. This reduces the time in the field to three days and can be of much years when the weather is bad. However, it costs fuel, and requires extra facilities and handling. Barn drying or curing is the best way of preventing mould.

Grass Used

The fields used have often not to be grazed during the season. However, some farmers top dress with nitrogen, graze off the field in spring and then top dress again with nitrogen after shutting up the field for hay. A total of 160 - 180 kg/ha (140 - 160 lb/acre) of nitrogen is used. The fields are then harvested after 50 - 60 days and can produce about five tonnes/ha DM (two tons/acre).

Chemical Preservatives

These are an alternative to barn drying. The chemicals control microbial activity and respiration of the hay. Proprionic acid can be used but gives off obnoxious fumes and can burn unprotected skin. The problems have been solved by the production of another form of the acid ammonium diproprionate (or ammonium propanoate). Even distribution is important but difficult to achieve.

Lucerne Hay

Field-dried lucerne hay tends to contain no ammonia but there is no heat damage either as occurs with drying in a high temperature drier. Lucerne tends to produce a high intake although the digestibility of the cell walls is less than that of grass. However, more of the lucerne is cell contents and these are highly digestible. The high level of protein and calcium has a buffering effect. Lucerne needs a deep, well-drained soil and should ideally be sown in April. The seed should be sown on ground which has not been used for lucerne in the previous 10 years in order to ensure the presence of the nodule bacterium. Cuts can be taken every six weeks. During the first three weeks a cut lucerne makes growth at the expense of the roots, in the second three weeks the root reserves are replenished. As potassium and phosphorus are lost in the crop, it is essential to use adequate potash and phosphate fertilisers.

Kale

The crop is little used for beef cattle, although it can provide the protein and some of the energy required by finishing cattle. It can also be introduced to calves from three months onwards at a level of 5 kg (11 lb) daily. The dry matter content is low (14 per cent) although the crude protein level is good (16 per cent) and it is highly digestible (70 per cent). The protein level tends to be higher the more leaf that is present.

TABLE 3.11

Yield of Different Kales

	Yield	
	tonnes/ha	tons/acre
Marrow stem	55	22
Normal thousand head	40	16
Dwarf thousand head	38	15

Kale is usually sown in May although it may be planted on land in June or July following a cut of grass for conservation in wetter areas. It is usually fed between mid-October and the end of December. The more frost-resistant thousand-headed kale can be used later in the winter. Kale can be used while it is frozen but once thawing occurs the plant will rot and so should not be fed. The kale can be fed by strip grazing in the field or coarse chopped with a forage harvester and fed in yards or on a well-drained concrete pad behind an electric fence and near the housing.

Fattening cattle (300 - 500 kg; 650 - 1100 lb) can gain satisfactorily on a diet of 20 kg (45 lb) kale, 6 kg (13 lb) hay and 2.5 kg (5.5 lb) barley daily.

Bloat can occur if large quantities of kale are fed and this can be overcome by ensuring that the crop is introduced slowly to the diet and by ensuring hay or straw is eaten prior to feeding the kale. Several minerals are deficient including phosphorus, copper, manganese and iodine and so a balanced mineral supplement is advisable. High calcium and low phosphorus can lead to infertility problems which can be overcome by a high phosphorus mineral supplement. Very heavy kale feeding can lead to poor growth rate and haematuria and in such circumstances the amount of the green crop fed should be immediately reduced. Prolonged heavy feeding of kale can result in anaemia. If fed in the field the hard stumps in the wet ground or very hard, frosted ground, can lead to lameness, particularly due to foul-in-the-foot.

Cabbages

These are occasionally fed. Their feeding values are similar to those of kale. The dry matter content is usually low (11 per cent) but the protein content is often over 20 per cent with a high digestibility of 68 - 71 per cent.

Straw

Wheat Straw

This is mainly used for bedding. It tends to be of little use for feeding as it is highly lignified, coarse and with a low digestibility. The yield of straw is about 4 tonnes/ha (1.6 tons/acre).

Oat Straw

This is highly acceptable as a feed to animals. The total area of oats is only 0.15 million ha (0.38 million acres) with a yield of 2.5 tonnes/ha (1 ton/acre). Most oats are grown in the north and west of Britain.

Barley Straw

This is often used for feed. The yield of straw is 2.5 tonnes/ha (1 ton/acre). Spring-sown barleys tend to have a higher digestibility than those of autumn. Digestibility is about 46 per cent for spring and 42 per cent for winter barleys. Ideally the straw should be clean, bright and well-harvested. When the straw has been lying and is weathered and discoloured digestibility is reduced by eight per cent or more (M.A.F.F. Advisory Leaflet 551, 1977).

TABLE 3.12

Barley Straw Analysis

	Dry Matter %	Digestibility %	Metabolisable Energy mJ/kg DM	Crude Protein % DM	Digestible Crude Protein % DM
Good	86	49	7.3	3.8	1.0
Medium	86	45	6.7	3.7	0.9
Poor	86	41	6.1	3.7	0.8

Straw is too low in digestibility, metabolisable energy, protein, minerals and vitamins to provide a maintenance diet. In finishing cattle, intensive beef systems can use straw at 1 kg (2 lb) level with *ad libitum* concentrates. In older finishing animals, small amounts of straw (2 - 3 kg; 4.5 - 6.5 lb) are often fed as well as other roughage and measured amounts of concentrates. In store cattle 3 - 4 kg (6.5 - 9.0 lb) of straw may be fed together with other feeds.

Chopped Straw

Straw can be mechanically chopped to 50 - 80 mm (2 - 3 in) and has an improved digestibility.

Milled Straw

This also has improved digestibility but does require considerable energy in its production (see page 62).

Treated Straw

See page 63.

Brewers' Grains

Brewers' grains are a by-product of beers, ales, malt and stout. They are rich in protein and fibre but have a reduced energy level. The grains may be sold wet or dried. One kilogram (2 lb) of dry grains is equivalent to 4 kg (9 lb) wet grains. The grains can become mouldy and so they must be fed fresh. The grains should not be exposed to the air for long periods before feeding and if more than a few days' supply is kept, they should be stored in airtight conditions to prevent souring or moulding. Storage in a sealed heap will allow the grains to be kept for about two or three weeks but it can be fed at a level of 2.5 kg (5.5 lb) from four months old. Grains can also be ensiled but it is essential that sealing is adequate.

When grains are in adequate supply, levels of 20 kg (45 lb) can be fed daily to fattening cattle with hay and barley. Yearlings can receive 5 - 7 kg (11 - 15 lb) daily. Use for young calves is not recommended.

Sugar Beet Pulp

Sugar beet pulp is produced from sugar beet. Following its shredding and removal of the sugar, over half a million ton(ne)s of dried pulp are produced in Great Britain annually. Wet beet pulp has a very high moisture level and is the fresh by-product after the sugar has been extracted. The water is usually removed with heavy presses and results in pressed pulp (18 *per cent* DM) and molassed pressed pulp (25 *per cent* DM).

TABLE

Feeding Value of Sugar Beet Pulp

	Dry Matter %	Metabolisable Energy mJ/kg DM	DCP % DM	Crude Protein
Wet pulp	9	12.7	6.6	10.6
Pressed pulp	18	12.7	6.6	10.6
Molassed pressed pulp	25	12.0	10.6	17.7
Dried molassed pulp	90	12.2	6.1	10.6

Both types of pressed pulp are usually distributed close to sugar beet factories and they tend to lose their nutritional value and palatability on exposure to air. It can be stored up to two weeks provided air is excluded by covering the pulp, otherwise it is best kept in airtight containers. When beet pulp is to be transported over distances it is usually dried to about 90 *per cent* DM and molasses added. About 90 *per cent* of beet pulp is supplied as dried molassed sugar beet pulp, mainly in the shredded form or as beet pulp nuts.

In calves between three and six months 0.5 kg (1 lb) of beet pulp can be fed, rising to 1.4 kg (3 lb). In growing and finishing cattle dried sugar beet pulp can be fed with hay or silage. Between 2 and 4 kg (4 - 9 lb) can be given daily.

Anabolic Steroids

Anabolic agents used in beef production are shown in Table 3.14 and their use is given in Table 3.15.

TABLE 3.14

Anabolic Agents Used in Beef Production

Compound	Dose	Trade Name	Manufacturer	Minimum Withdrawal Period
Oestradiol + Testosterone	20 mg 200 mg	Implixa BF	Hoechst UK	90 days
Oestradiol + Progesterone	20 mg 200 mg	Implixa BM	Hoechst UK	90 days
Oestradiol	45 mg	Compudose 365	Elanco	None
Oestradiol benzoate + Progesterone	20 mg 200 mg	Synovex S	Syntex	None
Oestradiol benzoate + Testosterone proprionate	20 mg 200 mg	Synovex H	Syntex	None
Trenbolone acetate	300 mg	Finaplix	Hoechst UK	60 days
Zeranol	36 mg	Ralgro	Crown Chemical Co	70 days

All are concerned with anabolism, i.e. increased muscle formation and improved feed conversion efficiency.

TABLE 3.15

The Type of Anabolic Agents Used in Beef Production

Trade Name	Legal Category	Target Animals	Presentation
Compudose 365	POM	Steers	Silicone rubber cylinders
Finaplix	POM	Heifers, steers, cull cows	15 yellow pellets
Implixa BF	POM	Female veal calves, intensively-reared female beef animals	10 white tablets
Implixa BM	POM	Male veal calves, intensively-reared male beef animals	10 white tablets
Ralgro	(POM)*	Cattle of any age	3 yellow pellets
Synovex H	POM	Female cattle	8 white pellets
Synovex S	POM	Steers	8 yellow pellets

*The category for this product has been PML but a recommendation has been made to have it regarded as POM.

These compounds tend to be used in about a third of all cattle being reared for beef. There are three types of compound:

Androgenic - Testosterone, trenbolone acetate

Oestrogenic - Oestradiol, zeranol

Progestogenic - Progesterone

Zeranol is not a true anabolic steroid as it does not possess a steroid ring in its structure and so it is often referred to as an anabolic agent. In other countries an implant of 20 mg oestradiol benzoate and 140 mg trenbolone acetate (Revalor - Roussel-Uclaf) is available.

The compounds used should be of the opposite type of hormones to those already in the animal, i.e. in bulls use female hormones, in steers use male and female hormones and in heifers use male hormones. Usually a greater effect of using an anabolic steroid is seen the more intensive the system being used. Thus they are best used when cattle are being finished on cereals or are in intensive cereal beef systems. The compounds are inserted subcutaneously in the ear and towards its base. When the compounds are used then any minimum implant to slaughter period must be observed.

The compounds should not be used in heifers or bulls intended for breeding. Occasionally side-effects are seen and these can include virilism, delayed puberty, increased dystokia levels, impaired udder development and reduced milk yield. In steers the problems can include excessive bulling, riding, udder development, raised tail head, prolapsed penis and aggression.

TABLE 3.16

Availability of Anabolic Agents in Europe

	Legalised Use		
Oestradiol	UK	Eire	Germany
Progesterone	UK	Eire	Germany
Testosterone	UK	Eire	Germany
Trenbolone	UK	Eire	France
Zeranol	UK	Eire	France

Recently use of female hormones in bulls has increased liveweight gain, reduced aggressive behaviour and reduced testicular development. In some cases the conformation of bull carcases has been improved and there has been improved fat cover of the carcase. Tests are now available to detect the presence of anabolic steroids and are usually based on thin layer chromatography and radioimmunoassay. In the EEC the use of stilbene derivatives such as diethylstilboestrol, hexoestrol and dienoestrol is not permitted.

The European Economic Community has been considering the use of anabolic steroids. At present, while allowing the controlled use of oestradiol, testosterone and progesterone, it is against the further utilisation of trenbolone and zeranol. This is likely to affect the contents of Table 3.16.

Growth Promoters

Monensin Sodium (Romensin, Elanco)

This is an ionophore antibiotic which alters rumen fermentation by increasing the conversion of formic acid to proprionic acid rather than producing methane. It can be used for animals at grass as well as those receiving some concentrates. There is increased feed conversion efficiency and in some cases there is a slight reduction in feed intake. Reduced appetite may occur if monensin is introduced too quickly, especially to heavy cattle. The compound can be used in all beef cattle following the start of rumination and beef and dairy heifers up to the time of service. If fed in the last 60 days before slaughter the level of feeding should be about half the recommended level. There is no withdrawal period.

TABLE 3.17

Type of Feed	Concentration of Monensin (ppm)	Monensin Intake
Complete feed	20 - 40	
Supplementary feeding		
Ruminating - 250 kg (550 lb) BW		125 mg/head/day
250 - 450 kg (550 - 1000 lb) BW		250 mg/head/day
Over 450 kg (1000 lb) BW		360 mg/head/day
Pasture feeding		200 mg/head/day

Avoparcin

This antibiotic is used as a growth promoter and is used at a level of 20 - 40 ppm in calf feeds (Avotan, Cyanamid). It is now available for use in beef animals of any age and can be fed at 15 - 45 ppm.

Ronnel

This organophosphorus compound has been used successfully in America to increase growth rate with improved feed conversion efficiency. The maximum response was obtained at 80 ppm of diet or at 2 mg/kg BW. The mode of action has been considered to be due to an alteration in thyroid function with the production of increased quantities of circulating thyroxine (T_4) but with no effect on tri-iodothyronine (T_3), cortisol or aldosterone.

Bambermycin (Flavomycin, Fisons)

This antibiotic is also a growth promoter and can be included in calf feeds. It is also used for beef cattle up to slaughter and can be included in concentrates, mineral supplement, or feed block. Various products are available. The levels of bambermycin used are shown in Table 3.18.

TABLE 3.18

Levels of Bambermycin Used

Type of Cattle/Feed	Maximum Age	Level of Bambermycin (ppm)
Calves		
Milk replacer	6 months	8 - 16
Dry feed	6 months	6 - 16
Fattening Cattle		
Concentrate	-	2 - 10
Feed blocks	-	80

The antibiotic can be fed to growing heifers up to the time of first service but should not be given to adult breeding stock.

Lasalocid

Lasalocid is an ionophore antibiotic and has been used experimentally for promoting cattle growth. It forms the active ingredient of an anticoccidial premix (Comben, 1984).

Salinomycin

This is another ionophore antibiotic which has been undergoing feed trials in cattle.

References

COMBEN, N (1984) Veterinary Record, 114, 128.

MEAT AND LIVESTOCK COMMISSION (1978) Grazing Management. Beef Production Handbook No. 4. Meat and Livestock Commission, Bletchley. pp. 1-44.

MINISTRY OF AGRICULTURE, FISHERIES AND FOOD (1977) Straw as a Feeding Stuff. Leaflet 551. MAFF, Pinner. pp. 1-7.

MINISTRY OF AGRICULTURE, FISHERIES AND FOOD (1982a) Grass Silage: Quality and Feeding. Leaflet 494. MAFF, Alnwick. pp. 1-11.

MINISTRY OF AGRICULTURE, FISHERIES AND FOOD (1982b) Grazing Management for Beef Cattle. Grassland Practice, No. 11, Booklet 2051, MAFF, Alnwick. pp. 1-18.

MINISTRY OF AGRICULTURE, FISHERIES AND FOOD (1983b) Silage Effluent. Farm Waste Management. Booklet 2429, MAFF, Alnwick. pp. 1-10.

PAIN, D F and BROOM, D M (1978) Animal Production, 26, 75-83.

CHAPTER 4

INTENSIVE BEEF PRODUCTION

Cereal Beef

This production method is often known as barley beef, because of the usual cereal fed, or the Rowett system, because of its development by Dr. T. Preston at the Rowett Research Institute. It was devised in the early 1960's at a time of relatively cheap cereal prices. At present prices of barley are much higher and in consequence the system has high cash inputs. However, it is still used and probably amounts to about five *per cent* of total beef production. The system aims to produce finished animals at 10 to 12 months old, at a slaughter weight of 385 - 410 kg (850 - 900 lb) for steers, which means a daily liveweight gain in the region of 1.1 kg (2.5 lb). Animals reared on the system often command a financial premium.

Type of Animal

As large amounts of cereal are fed, the animals used must be late-maturing. Thus male cattle, either entire or castrate, are used. The animals tend to be of dairy-bred type (i.e. born on dairy farms) such as Friesians, or the beef bulls crossed onto a Friesian cow. Most of the sires used tend to be of Continental type, e.g. Charolais, Limousin, Blonde d'Aquitaine or Simmental, although some indigenous breeds have been used successfully, e.g. South Devon, and possibly the Lincoln Red, Devon or Sussex. Early-maturing breeds, such as Aberdeen Angus or Hereford, are unsatisfactory when used to produce steers.

The System (see Table 4.1)

Calf Rearing

The calves are bought at any time of the year. They are reared on a milk substitute diet either fed restrictedly by bucket or *ad libitum* by dispensing machine or reservoir system (see Calf Management and Disease Notes). Weaning usually takes place at five weeks of age. In order to ensure that the animals are eating sufficient concentrate and thereby avoid a marked check in weight gain at weaning, the use of a bucket system with abrupt weaning is probably better than the *ad libitum* system. If the latter is used and early weaning is to be practised, it is best to provide the milk substitute for decreasing periods during the last two weeks prior to weaning. The calves are bedded on straw, and hay and water should be offered within four days of arrival. In the case of *ad libitum* milk-fed calves, solid feed will be consumed late. An early weaning concentrate containing about 17 *per cent* crude protein is used and weaning can occur abruptly when 0.7 kg (1.5 lb) has been consumed daily for three consecutive days by bucket fed calves. Once the calves are used to eating dry feed, some farmers change to a cheaper early weaning concentrate mix.

As the animals will be slaughtered at under a year old, disbudding is not always undertaken. Castration is also often not practised, but when it is, it usually takes place between four and eight weeks old. Castration over two months of age requires the use of an anaesthetic and must be performed by a veterinary surgeon.

TABLE 4.1

Projected Weight Gains for Friesian Steers on Cereal Beef Systems

Age	Daily Weight Gain kg/day	Daily Weight Gain lb/day	Feed Conversion Ratio	Feed Conversion Efficiency
Birth to 6 weeks	0.45	1.0	-	-
6 weeks to 3 months	0.95	2.1	3.2	0.31
3 to 6 months	1.2	2.7	4.3	0.23
6 months to slaughter	1.3	2.9	6.6	0.15
Overall	1.1	2.5	5.5	0.18

(After Meat and Livestock Commission, 1977)

Growing Period

At a weight of 90 - 100 kg (198 - 220 lb), when the calves are about 10 to 12 weeks old, then they are gradually introduced to a diet predominantly consisting of rolled barley, but which provides 14.5 per cent crude protein as well as a vitamin and mineral mix. The amount of protein supplementation depends on the protein content of the barley, which can be made up with a high protein (40 per cent crude protein) or a normal protein (34 per cent) supplement. Urea can be used as a part-substitute for vegetable protein at this stage.

Finishing Period

As protein supplementation is expensive, once the cattle reach 250 kg (550 lb), which is at about six months old, the protein content can be reduced to 12 per cent. High protein barley will not need to be supplemented at this stage and, where such additions are necessary, they can just be in the form of urea. The animals are slaughtered at 385 - 410 kg (850 - 900 lb) with a carcase weight of 205 - 240 kg (450 - 525 lb).

Feed

Barley

Barley has a high metabolisable energy value of 13.7 mJ/kg DM and a dry matter content of above 80 per cent. Cereal with a moisture content of less than 16 per cent should have moisture added, usually in the form of steam, before being rolled or crimped. However, cereal with a moisture content of at least 16 per cent can be fed rolled. Use of whole barley grains results in wastage through reduced digestibility. Pelleting the diet can cause increased feed efficiency, but it is expensive.

Roughage

Hay is often fed in the calf period although good quality barley straw has been successfully substituted. Preserving the husk on the barley grain will also help increase roughage levels and so grinding is not advisable. Roughage should be provided to help prevent liver abscesses, acidosis, bloat or insufficient processing of the cereals. Usually 1 kg (2 lb) of hay per day is sufficient. If no feeding racks are available and straw is provided in the form of bedding, then at least 2 kg (4.5 lb) per animal should be given.

Vitamin/Mineral Supplements

Vitamin A should be provided at the level of at least six million International Units per tonne to ensure adequate amounts for these rapidly growing cattle (see Table 4.2).

TABLE 4.2

Composition of a Vitamin/Mineral Supplement for Cereal Beef

	% Composition of Supplement	Mixed Feed	
		kg/tonne	lb/ton
Limestone	50%	13	28
Salt	24%	6	13.5
Steamed bone flour	20%	5	11
Iron	0.5%	135 g	4.5 oz
Zinc	0.26%	75 g	2.5 oz
Copper	336 ppm	8 ppm	8 ppm
Cobalt	45 ppm	1 ppm	1 ppm
Iodine	5 ppm	0.1 ppm	0.1 ppm
Vitamin A	265,000 iu/kg	6,750,000 iu	6,750,000 iu
Vitamin D_3	65,000 iu/kg	1,700,000 iu	6,750,000 iu

(After Meat and Livestock Commission, 1974)

TABLE 4.3

Performance Characteristics for Cereal Beef from Friesian Steers

Daily gain	1.2 kg	2.6 lbs
Slaughter age	345 days	
Weight at slaughter	404 kg	889 lbs
Carcase weight	211 kg	464 lbs
Killing-out percentage	52.2%	
Lean percentage of carcase	61.0%	
High-priced cuts (percentage)	41.4%	
Concentrates fed	1.88 tonnes	1.85 tons

(After Meat and Livestock Commission, 1977)

Buildings

No special buildings are required except in the calf rearing period. Space per calf should be about 0.9 - 1.4 m^2 (10 - 15 ft^2). Care must be taken to ensure adequate ventilation levels. The cattle are best housed in groups of about 20. Usually straw yards are used, minimum area per animal from 230 - 450 kg (505 - 990 lb) of 1.9 - 4.0 m^2 (20 - 43 ft^2), or slats with an area per beast of 1.4 - 2.3 m^2 (15 - 25 ft^2). Concentrates are fed *ad libitum* from a minimum space of 75 mm (3 in) per beast with water bowls distributed one per 15 cattle or 2000 mm^2 (3.2 in^2) each of water trough space.

Advantages

1. It is possible to enter into contracts to produce a regular supply of beef.
2. The capital requirements are relatively low.
3. The performance is predictable and can be easily measured and costed.
4. Except at calf stage, the labour demand is low.
5. There are no direct requirements for land.
6. Useful system for farmers producing own cereal and straw.
7. It is often possible to negotiate premiums for bull beef.

Disadvantages

1. Very sensitive to price of calf. (The calf is equivalent to about 20 *per cent* of total returns.)
2. Very sensitive to price of barley. (The cereal is equivalent to about 50 to 55 *per cent* of total returns).
3. System requires buildings.
4. As the animals become older, so their feed conversion efficiency declines, especially over 360 kg (750 lb) and so timing of slaughter is important.

Veterinary Problems

Most problems are in the calf period:-

1. Bought-in calves usually from market and/or dealer.
2. Thus colostrum status not known.
3. Enteric problems.
4. Possibility of salmonellosis.
5. Enzootic pneumonia.
6. Mortality in calf period about 4.7 *per cent*.

Rearing and finishing periods:-

1. Bloat.
2. Laminitis.
3. Liver abscesses.

4. Foul-of-the-foot.
5. Infectious bovine rhinotracheitis.
6. Acidosis, ruminitis.
7. Blackleg.
8. Infectious bovine keratoconjunctivitis (New Forest eye).
9. Urea poisoning.
10. Ringworm.
11. Pediculosis.
12. Warts.
13. Overall mortality about 6.6 per cent (Meat and Livestock Commission, 1976) can range from 0 to 6.6 per cent.
14. If bedded in straw yards there is often considerable overgrowth of feet.
15. Insufficient bedding can lead to the animals' skin becoming covered in faeces and this can cause considerable problems at slaughter in ensuring that the carcase does not become contaminated.
16. Mortality in rearing finishing period about 2.0 per cent.
17. Culling in rearing finishing period from digestive/respiratory problems about 5.0 per cent.

Alternatives and Improvements to Cereal Beef

The returns obtained with cereal beef can be improved by:

1. The use of bulls instead of steers (see below).
2. The incorporation of cheaper feeds (see page 61).
3. The use of anabolic steroids (see page 48).
4. Use of other growth promoters (see page 50).
5. Obtaining premiums for the steady supply of superior quality beef.

1. Use of Bulls

As bulls are later maturing than steers they can be reared for a longer period on a higher energy diet before reaching the required level of finish, i.e. fat cover for slaughter. Their daily liveweight gain tends to be better (about 11 per cent), as does their feed conversion efficiency (7 per cent). They also produce a heavier (9.5 per cent) and leaner (2.5 per cent) carcase than the castrate. Their growth rate is such that slaughter weight is usually reached earlier than for steers (2 per cent less), but their concentrate usage tends to be higher (2.5 per cent). Gross margins for bulls are often 33 to 55 per cent better than for steers. When bulls and steers are slaughtered at the same age, carcases of the former tend to be between 20 and 30 kg (45 and 65 lb) heavier for only an extra 50 kg (1 cwt) of concentrates.

Buildings

The handling and housing of bulls is covered by a Code of Practice. The cost of buildings to meet the requirements is high. The animals may be kept on slats or straw yards. It is suggested that stocking rates are best high with a maximum level at finishing of 4.0 m^2 (43 ft^2) per beast in straw yards and 2.3 m^2 (25 ft^2) per beast on slats. Many farmers find the use of slats beneficial as the animals are less sure-footed on them and are therefore quieter. In addition, stockmen do not need to enter pens for bedding down.

Many animals used in cereal beef are kept entire. This recognises the merits of bulls and as rearing is in buildings, the statutory regulations can usually be met. Bulls are routinely reared in many countries throughout Europe.

Disadvantages

1. Rearing problems. It must always be remembered that bulls are being dealt with. They should be kept in small groups (under 20 - Paragraph 54, MAFF/DAFS/WOAD Code of Recommendations for the Welfare of Livestock - Cattle, 1983). Once a group is formed it should not be upset. If a bull is removed from the group it should not be returned. If it is necessary to take out an animal and return it then it should be removed with some others and returned with the others. Two people should always be present when working with bulls. Besides not adding bulls to already-formed groups, one group should not be added to another when the animals are turned out to grass or are being sent for slaughter. Groups of bulls should be kept at a safe distance from female cattle (Paragraph 54, MAFF/DAFS/WOAD Code of Recommendations for the Welfare of Livestock - Cattle, 1983).

2. Buildings must be of sufficient strength to house bulls. Escape areas should be available. Provision should always be available to allow easy movement of bulls from pen to pen and to loading areas or weighing without them mixing with other bulls. The Code of Recommendations for the Welfare of Livestock - Cattle (MAFF/DAFS/WOAD, 1983 - Paragraph 55) states that suitable handling facilities for bulls are essential and warns that it may be necessary to give special attention to the strengthening of housing and fencing.

3. A Code of Practice exists for bull beef production which meets Health and Safety Executive requirements. Buildings for bull beef should be registered with the Executive before the animals reach eight months old. The British Code of Practice states that the pen should have fencing at least 1.5 m (5 ft) high with the lower 1 m (3¼ ft) such that a child cannot get his head or body through the mesh. The gates to the buildings should be 1.5 m (5 ft) high and again the lower 1 m (3¼ ft) made child-proof. Notices should be placed on the outside stating "Danger - Bulls - Keep Out". Feeding should be from outside the pen.

4. Bullish characteristics of carcase. There is a slightly higher proportion of meat in the forequarter than in steers because of the neckcrest. However, because the killing-out percentage of bulls is better and therefore the carcase weighs more, the weight of meat in the hind quarter still tends to be more than the steer.

5. Bull carcases tend to be leaner and often have less fat cover. This can at times lead to complaints of lack of finish in bull carcases. Also the lighter fat cover tends to make the meat seem a deeper colour.

TABLE 4.4

Projected Weight Gains for Friesian Bulls on Cereal Beef Systems

Age	Daily Weight Gain kg/day	Daily Weight Gain lb/day	Feed Conversion Ratio	Feed Conversion Efficiency
Birth to 6 weeks	0.45	1.0	-	-
6 weeks to 3 months	1.0	2.2	2.7	0.37
3 to 6 months	1.3	2.9	4.0	0.25
6 months to slaughter	1.4	3.1	6.1	0.16
Overall	1.2	2.6	4.8	0.21

(After Meat and Livestock Commission, 1977)

TABLE 4.5

Performance Characteristics of Cereal Beef from Friesian Bulls

	kg	lb
Daily gain	1.3	2.9
Slaughter age	338 days	
Weight to slaughter	445	980
Carcase weight	231	508
Killing-out percentage	51.9 %	
Lean percentage of carcase	66.3%	
High-priced cuts (%)	41.5%	
Concentrates fed	1.93 tonnes	1.9 tons

(After Meat and Livestock Commission, 1977)

TABLE 4.6

The Composition of Friesian Bull and Steer Carcases on Cereal Beef Systems

	Percentage Bulls	Percentage Steers
Lean	66.3%	61.0%
Fat	16.6%	22.5%
Bone	15.6%	15.0%

6. Dark cutting of meat is particularly seen in bulls. This occurs if the animals are excited at the rearing farm, during transport or at the abattoir. It leads to the rapid utilisation of the glycogen reserves. Once the animals are killed the lack of glycogen results in limited rigor mortis and setting of the carcase. The pH of the meat after slaughter usually falls after death but this is not the case when glycogen has been utilised. In consequence the meat remains at a higher pH and this alters the refractive index of the meat, allowing light to penetrate deeper and thereby give the dark colour which may even appear black. The problem is not detrimental to the meat other than that the keeping qualities are slightly reduced. However, the meat tends to be rejected by the consumer and so has to be used for manufacturing, thereby lessening its potential value. The problem can be overcome by reducing stress before slaughter. Ensure groups destined for slaughter have been together for at least 10 days. Do not mix groups at the time of going for slaughter on the farm, in transport or at the abattoir. Try to ensure the animals are slaughtered on entry to the abattoir. If bulls have to enter the lairage, make sure they are not in close proximity to heifers or cows. They should be kept there for two days with water and food provided. The use of glucose in the lairage water may also overcome some of the problem of dark cutting.

7. Many slaughtermen and slaughterhouses are reluctant to deal with bulls. However, those abattoirs which do deal with such animals soon produce a satisfactory routine and find benefits in killing-out percentage, percentage lean, etc.

Legislation Affecting Bull Beef

Health and Safety at Work Act 1974

There are obligations placed on employers as well as the self-employed and employees to ensure that they do not put at risk the health and safety of themselves or others. Her Majesty's Agricultural Inspectorate at the local office of the Health and Safety Executive can advise on standards of safety for bull beef production.

Transit of Animals (Road and Rail) Order 1975

Bulls over 10 months old must be separated from other stock during transport and must be individually tied by the head or neck. However, bulls more than 10 months old which have been reared in groups on a beef unit may be carried together in one individual vehicle without being tied.

Market (Protection of Animals) Order 1964-1965

This states that all bulls over 10 months old must be separated from other animals and secured by the head or neck.

Local Government Acts 1933-1972

District councils have powers to introduce bylaws which prevent the presence of bulls in any field through which there is a public footpath.

2. Incorporation of Cheaper Feeds

Various methods of cheapening the ration can be produced. These involve various substitutes for the energy or protein part of the ration.

Energy Substitutes

(a) Maize Silage

See Pages 67-68.

(b) Oats

These have a low energy content with an ME of 11.5 mJ/kg DM but the dry matter level is similar at 86.9 per cent. They can be used to completely replace barley in the ration. However this tends to result in an increased dry matter intake with a reduction in feed conversion ratio of about seven per cent. This can result in about 0.4 kg/ lb extra feed per kg/lb gain. In addition there is greater gut fill resulting in about a two per cent decrease in killing-out percentage.

(c) Wheat

Wheat has a slightly higher metabolisable energy (14 mJ/kg DM) than barley and a similar dry matter content (86 per cent). However it does lack fibre and this can be overcome by the inclusion of 15 per cent oats. Pelleted rations can have 65 per cent of the barley substituted by oats but if the ration is to be fed loose, the maximum inclusion rate of oats should be 50 per cent.

(d) Maize Grain

This also has a high energy value (14.2 mJ/kg DM) and a similar dry matter content (86 per cent) to barley. When pelleted, maize can successfully replace up to 65 per cent of the barley. However, when fed loose a level of 50 per cent is considered suitable. Ground maize tends to be rejected by cattle and so it is best fed as cracked grains. When fed for long periods body-fat becomes a cream colour rather than the usual white. Occasionally the cob and corn - ground maize ears - are ensiled and have a high digestibility and energy value similar to barley, although dry matter content is less (30 to 50 per cent).

(e) Sugar Beet Pulp

This can be fed as mineralised pulp nuts or molassed sugar beet pulp (ME 12.2 mJ/kg DM) with a dry matter of 90.2 per cent. Dry matter intake tends to rise and so animals finish quicker. The sugar beet pulp can be substituted for about 50 per cent of the barley, but care must be taken to ensure cattle do not selectively eat the former in the ration. As animals fatten more quickly, they may contain more abdominal fat.

(f) Ground Straw

Barley straw has a low metabolisable energy (7.3 mJ/kg DM) when compared with barley but its digestibility can be increased by milling. The inclusion of 20 per cent milled straw with the barley will not alter weight gains but the process of milling is expensive and there is a reduction in feed conversion efficiency. The straw also ensures increased gut fill and so the carcase killing-out percentage is decreased. Thus the straw must cheapen the cost of the ration by at least 30 to 40 per cent to be worthwhile. Straw can be fed as pellets or loose but in the latter case molasses (5.0 to 7.5 per cent) should be added to ensure adequate uptake (MLC Handbook, 1974). Milled straw with barley can result in bloat problems.

(g) Turnips

There are two types of turnip, those with white and those with yellow flesh. Both have a low dry matter content (nine per cent), with the white-fleshed type being lower, and a moderate energy level (11.2 mJ/kg DM). There tends to be a reduction in dry matter intake of turnips over the changeover period which results in reduced weight gains during this time. Substitution of up to a third of the dry matter intake with turnips produces no problem. In young animals the level should not exceed 50 per cent but, in adults, barley can be total replacement. However, there will be a period of adaptation and reduced weight gain during this time on diets of this type. The urine output of cattle will increase if the dietary dry matter contains over 50 per cent turnips. There tends to be little difference in uptake whether whole or sliced turnips are fed. Hoppers can be produced for feeding the turnips (MLC Handbook, 1974). Cases of choke are always possible on such a diet. The yield is about five tons/hectare (2 tons/acre) dry matter or actual yield of 6.13 tonnes/ha (25 tons/acre) for yellow flesh and a dry matter of 4.8 tonnes/ha (1.9 tons/acre) with a fresh weight of 68 tonnes/ha (27 tons/acre) for white-fleshed turnips.

(h) Swedes

These have a slightly higher dry matter (12 per cent) and energy (12.8 mJ/kg DM) content than turnips. The information under turnips is also applicable to swedes. They can be distinguished from turnips by their distinct neck. The yield is about 7.1 tonnes/hectare (2.8 tons/acre) dry matter or 75 tonnes/hectare (30 tons/acre) actual weight.

(i) Mangels

Most of the bulbous part of the root in English varieties grows above the ground and can be lifted by hand or fodder root harvesters. English types have less dry matter than some of the continental types which tend to grow more deeply in the soil. The yield is about 12.8 tonnes/hectare (5 tons/acre) dry matter and the average dry matter is 12 per cent (range 10 to 15 per cent), giving an actual yield of 120 tonnes/ha (48 tons/acre).

(j) Fodder Beet

Those with the highest dry matter content have deepest roots. On average it is 17 per cent but can vary between 14 and 20 per cent, giving a yield of 14.8 tonnes/hectare (6 tons/acre) dry matter or an actual yield of 85 tonnes/hectare (34 tons/acre).

(k) Potatoes

Another crop similar in most circumstances to swedes or turnips. The dry matter at 21 per cent is higher than for the other two crops and the energy level is 12.5 mJ/kg DM. Potatoes tend to produce a higher dry matter intake and a higher daily liveweight gain than do equivalent levels of swedes. Choke can be a problem.

(l) Dried Grass Pellets

This is artificially dried and pelleted to produce a 90 per cent dry matter and 10.6 mJ/kg DM energy level. As the amount of dried grass in the diet increases, the fat content and killing-out percentage decrease. Higher levels of dry grass cause the fat to become more yellow. In some instances the pellets break up, producing a lot of dust and thereby wastage, while on other occasions the pellets are very hard, resulting in rejection. The diets can lead to bloat unless long stem roughage is available. When buying dried grass it is always best to use material of declared digestibility and from first cut spring herbage.

(m) Treated Straw

The digestibility of straw can be increased from 50 to about 60 per cent by the addition of 4 to 6 per cent sodium hydroxide. The equipment necessary is, however, expensive and uses much energy. The sodium hydroxide is caustic and so must be used with care. It freezes in the winter. Although the straw is used a few days after application and looks pleasant, it is less acceptable than ordinary straw. Use of the system usually results in animals drinking more and producing large quantities of alkaline urine. Salt-free feeds should be used.

Sodium hydroxide breaks down the basic cellulose in the straw, producing cellulose which can be digested by rumen bacteria. The improved digestibility of the straw means that the animal can eat more of the roughage. Successful alkali treatment involves chopping or grinding the straw to ensure adequate surface area is exposed, and the alkali must be evenly mixed. Wheat straw is easier to chop but does produce a lower ME of about 0.4 mJ/kg DM than barley straw.

Various methods of alkali treatment have been used including spraying 12 per cent caustic soda onto chopped straw, chopping straw and adding solid caustic soda, grinding the straw, mixing it with alkali and then cubing it, a 16 per cent solution has been added to ground straw in a feeder wagon. The equipment necessary to ensure a suitable diet is expensive but there are contract services available. The feed does have advantages in that a by-product is used and so there is no specific land requirement for its production. Dry matter intake does appear to increase when alkali-treated straw is mixed into a ration. The caustic soda and fibre both help to aid butter-fat production. The product is of a consistent quality and when mixed into a succulent feed it does provide a buffer ration for feeding at grass, particularly in dairy cattle. The treated straw is denser than untreated and so can be packed more tightly.

The main nutritional problem with sodium hydroxide-treated straw is that it does not contain much protein and so urea usually has to be added. As the dry matter content is very high it is best fed in a highly palatable feed such as brewers' grains or sugar beet pulp. Wet straw reduces the throughput of the machine, also tending to lead to uneven application and excessive heating with an increase in the likelihood of mould occurring. Handling the chemical can be difficult as it freezes in cold weather, and is extremely caustic and thus dangerous. However, provided all concerned with application take care, or a contractor is used, there is usually little problem.

Ammonium hydroxide has been shown to give similar results to sodium hydroxide and can be used in two different ways. The stack method involves the effective seating of a stack of about 20 ton(nes) prior to the injection under pressure of ammonia gas (anhydrous) or a solution of 32-35 per cent of ammonia in water (aqueous). The stack receives 28-35 kg (62-75 lb) ammonia per ton(ne) of straw and is then sealed for 6 to 8 weeks before it is opened and ventilated for several days. The oven method involves an airtight insulated chamber into which anhydrous ammonia is injected from a pressure tank. Treatment takes about 23 hours with the mixture circulated and heated to about 90°C for 15 hours, then a four-hour standstill period followed by a similar period when the gas is removed. The straw can be fed half-an-hour after removal from the oven. The method increases the digestibility by 14 to 15 per cent with a two- or three-fold rise in crude protein.

Protein Sources

Barley is a poor source of protein and so even when high protein levels are present in the cereal, protein supplementation must occur up to the six-month stage. In the early stages highly digestible protein, often of animal origin, is used. However, once animals reach three months old, cheaper sources of protein can start to be introduced.

(a) Urea

Besides utilising animal and vegetable proteins, micro-organisms in the rumen can make use of simpler nitrogenous products such as urea. Urea is converted to ammonia in the rumen and it is then absorbed and converted into bacterial protein. Many of the cheaper protein supplements on the market contain urea. They are usually in a pelleted form and can be added to the cereal. The use of NPN depends on the presence of a fully-developed ruminal microbial population and so it should not be used in animals until the rumen is completely functional, i.e. calves over three months old. Cattle over 100 kg (220 lb) (three months old) can receive part of their nitrogen requirements as urea. All the extra nitrogen requirement can be in this form from six months on. In growing animals the inclusion of up to 100 g (3.6 oz) of urea per day will at most reduce liveweight gains by five per cent compared with other protein sources. However, levels about 100 g (3.6 oz) can result in weight gain reductions greater than 10 per cent. The urea level of 100 g is equivalent to a one per cent level. Thus a usual daily feed intake of 7 kg (15 lb) supplies only 70 g (2.4 oz) of urea. If urea is included in diets on the farm it must be thoroughly mixed, otherwise there are dangers, with the possibility of urea poisoning.

(b) Dried Grass

The protein content of dried grass can provide a source of nitrogen. Some of the protein can be in the form of non-protein nitrogen. However, often, to provide sufficient protein with dried grass, the energy content of the ration will be reduced sufficiently to decrease weight gain. If

TABLE 4.7

Nutritional Values of Various Feeds Used in Cattle Diets

	Dry Matter %	Metabolisable Energy mJ/kg DM	Crude Protein % DM	Digestible Crude Protein % DM
Cereals				
Barley	86	13.7	9-11	8.2
Maize	86	14.2	10	7.8
Oats	86	11.5	11	8.4
Wheat	86	14.0	12	10.5
Roots and Green Feeds				
Swedes	12	12.8	11	9.1
Potatoes	21	12.5	9	4.7
Turnips	9	11.2	12	7.3
Dried lucerne	90	8.7	20	12.8
Dried poultry manure			27	
Field beans	86	12.8	25	20.9
Kale	14	11.0	16	12.3
Conserved Forages				
Dried grass	90	10.6	17	13.6
Good hay	85	9.0	10.0	5.8
Medium hay	85	8.4	8.5	3.9
Poor hay	85	7.5	9.2	4.5
Good silage	25	10.2	17.0	11.6
Medium silage	20	9.3	17.0	10.7
Poor silage	20	7.6	16.0	9.8
Maize silage	25	10.8	11.0	7.0
By-Products				
Fresh brewers' grains	22	10.0	20.5	14.9
Sugar beet pulp (molassed)	90	12.2	11.0	6.1
Ground straw (barley)	86	7.3	24	0.9
Protein Feeds				
Fish meal	90	11.1	70	63.1
Soyabean meal	90	12.3	52	45.3
Groundnut meal decorticated extracted	90	11.7	55	49.1
Urea (98%)			227	

the dried grass contains 20 per cent crude protein then an inclusion rate of 20 per cent is required to increase the total diet's crude protein level by only four per cent. The feed value depends on the grass and when cut.

(c) Dried Lucerne

This can be sold as dried grass and the comments are similar. About 12,000 hectares (30,000 acres) of lucerne are grown annually. Dried lucerne produced in a high-temperature drier results in some protein damage or denaturing. Thus only about half the protein is rumen-degradable and the rest is digested in the intestine.

(d) Dried Poultry Manure

This has been used in beef diets but does produce problems due to the variability of the product and its usual low energy level unless the manure contains much spilled feed. The crude protein level is usually in the range of 25 to 30 per cent. Poultry manure contains uric acid and so it should only be introduced slowly over a period of two to three weeks to prevent digestive upsets. A level of five per cent of dried poultry manure would increase the diet's crude protein level by 1.5 per cent. The product should not be confused with deep litter which contains large quantities of chopped straw and if used should be as a source of bulk or roughage (MLC Handbook, 1974).

(e) Field Beans

Various varieties of *Vicia faba* are used. The crude protein level of spring beans is better than winter beans. The moisture content is often over 15 per cent, making processing difficult. The beans are hard to incorporate into feeds by grinding as they tend to paste. Beans are slow to roll or mill. When included in rations it is best to use a 10 per cent level which produces about three per cent crude protein for the whole diet, although levels of 20 per cent have been fed without altering digestibility. However, high levels can result in digestive upsets and diarrhoea.

References

MEAT AND LIVESTOCK COMMISSION (1974) Handbook No. 2. Beef production: dairy-bred calves using cereals and arable products. Meat and Livestock Commission, Bletchley. pp. 1-60.

MEAT AND LIVESTOCK COMMISSION (1976) Cattle facts. A manual of economic standards. Meat and Livestock Commission, Bletchley. pp. 1-132.

MEAT AND LIVESTOCK COMMISSION (1977) Data Sheets. Meat and Livestock Commission, Bletchley. pp. 1-72.

MINISTRY OF AGRICULTURE, FISHERIES AND FOOD/DEPARTMENT OF AGRICULTURE AND FISHERIES FOR SCOTLAND/WELSH OFFICE AGRICULTURAL DEPARTMENT (1983) Codes of Recommendations for the Welfare of Livestock - Cattle. Leaflet 701. pp. 1-16.

Maize Silage Beef

The creation of hybrid varieties of maize has allowed the plant to be successfully grown in Britain. New early-maturing varieties include Leader, Bastille and Vivia. Maize is most successfully grown in the southern half of England, from below a line drawn between The Wash and Merseyside. It has uses in that it is usually sown in April/May at a time before silage-making. It produces a large quantity of dry matter per unit area (10 tonnes/ha; 4 tons/acre) with an average dry matter content of between 28 and 30 per cent. Harvesting is not critical and can be at any time between the "milk" and "late dough", although the latter is best as dry matter content is then higher. At the doughy stage the grain is dimpled with the lower plant leaves as well as the tips of the upper leaves being brown. Harvesting with older varieties occurred between October and November but new types allow gathering before mid-September, and require a precision crop harvester to ensure each grain is opened.

The crop is often used in a system similar to cereal beef although the energy content is less and protein levels are low. The amount of maize grown has declined in recent years from a record level of 40,000 hectares (100,000 acres) in 1977 to about 15,000 ha (37,500 acres) in 1982.

Type of Animal

The system suits dairy-bred male animals which can be either entire or castrated, although the best weight gains are with bulls. Cattle sired by early-maturing breeds (e.g. Hereford) are satisfactory for the system, as also are red breed crosses (e.g. Devon, Lincoln Red and Sussex). However, Friesians and Continental beef bull cross Friesian calves are most suitable.

The System (see Table 4.9)

Rearing Period

The animals receive *ad libitum* maize silage with a protein supplement from three months old. The silage is gradually introduced. The amount of protein required varies with age. Thus at three to six months the crude protein level should be 16.5 per cent (DCP 9.9 per cent) which can be reduced to 15 per cent (DCP 9.0 per cent) at six to nine months and then to 12 per cent (DCP 7.2 per cent) from nine months to slaughter. Satisfactory feeds can be obtained by use of Table 4.8.

TABLE 4.8

Satisfactory Maize Silage Feeding Systems

3-6 months	*Ad lib.* silage	+ 1½% urea + 20% dried lucerne	OR 1.5kg 35% crude protein supplement daily
6-9 months	*Ad lib.* silage	+ 1½% urea	OR 1.5kg 35% crude protein supplement daily
9 months - slaughter	*Ad lib.* silage		OR 1.5kg 35% crude protein supplement daily

Feed intake varies from about 12 kg (27 lb) at 135 kg (300 lb) liveweight to 40 kg (90 lb) at 455 kg (1,000 lb) liveweight. The animals, particularly if bulls, may require rolled barley in the finishing period. The amount of cereal required may be about 150 kg (330 lb) and is usually fed at about 2 kg (4.4 lb) per day. Cattle are usually slaughtered at a heavier weight and older age than with cereal beef. Slaughter is, in most cases, at about 1 year 2 months old, at a body weight of 450-500 kg (990-1100 lb).

TABLE 4.9

Performance Characteristics of Friesian Bulls and Steers on Maize Silage

	Bulls		Steers	
	kg	lb	kg	lb
Daily gain	1.0	2.2	0.95	2.1
Slaughter weight	500	1100	450	990
Slaughter age (months)	14		14	
Maize silage consumed DM	1.9 tonnes	1.9 tons	1.8 tonnes	1.8 tons
Stocking rate (beasts/area)	4.5/ha	1.8/acre	4.8/ha	1.9/acre

Feeding Procedure

Feed is usually presented in troughs or on the ground behind a feed barrier. The feeding space per animal should be about 0.6 m (2 ft) but if feeding is always *ad libitum* the space can be reduced by half to 0.3 m (1 ft) per beast. Feed can be delivered by means of a forage box or a mixer wagon. Feed is usually removed from the clamp by a fore-end loader.

Buildings

No special buildings are required but attention must be paid to ensure adequate ventilation. As animals are taken to a higher weight than cereal beef, the minimum space per beast at 450-540 kg (990-1190 lb) is 4.0-4.6 m^2 (43-50 ft^2) for straw and 1.9-2.6 m^2 (20-28 ft^2) on slats.

Advantages

1. Maize produces a large amount of dry matter per unit area (10 tonnes DM/ha; 4 tons/acre).
2. There is no direct use of land.
3. Sowing and harvesting can take place at times when labour is not engaged in other tasks, e.g. silage or hay-making, cereal harvesting.
4. A useful alternative to cereal beef.
5. It is possible to produce a regular supply of beef with a steady throughput.

6. Capital requirements tend to be relatively low and the system usually costs less than cereal beef.

7. Performance usually relatively predictable.

8. Labour demand low except during calf rearing and maize harvesting.

Disadvantages

1. In young animals there is a need for protein supplementation. Levels are considerably less than for cereals. Protein prices vary considerably at different times and can alter costs markedly.

2. The exposed face of the silage clamp undergoes considerable oxidation and thereby spoilage. Thus the face should be reduced by about 30 cm (12 ins) per day in summer and by 15 cm (6 ins) daily in winter.

3. Equipment for producing good quality precision-chopped silage is expensive but contractors can be hired.

4. When dry matter levels of the silage are less than 25 per cent then dry matter intakes tend to be low. In such situations weight gains can be assisted by feeding cereals such as rolled barley at 2-3 kg (4-6.5 lb) daily.

5. There can be a very variable yield and with some of the older varieties requiring harvesting in late autumn, there can be problems resulting from weather conditions.

6. The yellowing of the fat in intensive beef cattle may result in a loss of quality premium.

Veterinary Problems

1. Maize silage tends to be deficient in fat-soluble vitamins. When fed exclusively a supplement should be given per head consisting of 30,000 iu vitamin A, 6,000 iu vitamin D_3 and 300 iu vitamin E.

2. A ration exclusively of maize silage in growing cattle is deficient in calcium to the level of 10-20 g/day.

3. Slight deficiencies occur on maize silage of phosphorus and sodium. A supplement of 2 g of phosphorus should be given daily and for finishing animals 6 g of sodium is also required.

4. Trace elements tend to be deficient and finishing animals require 15 mg copper supplement per day.

5. Iodine, zinc and manganese are deficient in maize silage and should be supplemented.

6. Blackleg.

7. Infectious bovine keratoconjunctivitis (New Forest eye).

8. Urea poisoning.

9. Ringworm.

10. Pediculosis.

11. Warts.

12. If bedded on straw yards, feet may become overgrown.

13. If there is insufficient bedding the animals may become extremely dirty or soiled at the time of slaughter.

14. Bloat.
15. Laminitis.
16. Liver abscesses.
17. Foul-of-the-foot.
18. Acidosis, ruminitis.
19. Infectious bovine rhinotracheitis.

With bought-in calves, usually from dealers or market:

1. Often colostrum-deprived.
2. Enteric problems.
3. Salmonellosis.
4. Enzootic pneumonia.

References

MEAT AND LIVESTOCK COMMISSION (1974) Handbook No. 2. Beef production: dairy-bred calves using cereals and arable products. Meat and Livestock Commission, Bletchley. pp. 1-60.

MEAT AND LIVESTOCK COMMISSION (1976) Cattle facts. A manual of economic standards. Meat and Livestock Commission, Bletchley. pp. 1-132.

MEAT AND LIVESTOCK COMMISSION (1977) Data sheets. Meat and Livestock Commission, Bletchley. pp. 1-72.

MINISTRY OF AGRICULTURE, FISHERIES AND FOOD/DEPARTMENT OF AGRICULTURE AND FISHERIES FOR SCOTLAND/WELSH OFFICE AGRICULTURAL DEPARTMENT (1983) Codes of Recommendations for the Welfare of Livestock - Cattle. Leaflet 701. pp. 1-16.

CHAPTER 5

SEMI-INTENSIVE BEEF PRODUCTION

15-Month Grass - Cereal Beef

This is the least commonly used of the grass cereal beef systems and involves the use of large quantities of concentrates. The high cost of cereals reduces the attractiveness of the system.

Type of Animal

As large amounts of cereal are used the animal must be late-maturing. Male cattle are usually used and although mainly castrated, they could be entire provided the Codes of Practice are followed. The breeds used are most often dairy-bred in origin, Friesian or Charolais, Limousin, Simmental, or South Devon bulls crossed on a Friesian cow.

The System (see Table 5.1)

Calf Rearing

Calves to be used are born in the winter or early spring. They are weaned at five weeks and fed hay and concentrates containing 17 per cent crude protein. Summer-born calves have been used.

Grazing Period

The aim is to provide the cattle with as long a grazing period as possible so calves tend to be turned out at 12 weeks old or occasionally younger. Weight at turnout should be about 90 kg (200 lb). The animals should gain about 0.7 kg (1.5 lb) daily with some concentrate being introduced towards the end of the grazing season to maintain weight gain. Cattle should be about 210 kg (460 lb) at yarding.

Winter Finishing Period

Once housed a high concentrate diet is fed plus good quality silage or hay to gain about 1.1 kg (2.4 lb) daily. Slaughter is at a weight of 390-450 kg (860-990 lb) which is achieved at any time between 13 and 17 months old. The carcase weight is about 205-250 kg (450-550 lb).

Buildings

No special buildings are required except in the calf-rearing period. There is a need for calf pens on yards 0.9-1.4 m^2 (10-15 ft^2 and then follow-on housing 1.4-1.9 m^2 (15-20 ft^2). The second winter can be spent by the cattle in groups in straw yards with an area of 2.8-4.2 m^2 (30-40 ft^2) per 350-500 kg (770-1,100 lb) animal. If slatted yards are used, 1.4-2.3 m^2 (15-25 ft^2) are necessary and there should be 500 mm (20 ins) trough space per beast. One water bowl should be provided per 15 animals maximum, with 2,000 mm^2 (3.2 ins^2) of space per beast if troughs are used.

Advantages

1. The capital requirements are relatively low.
2. The performance is relatively predictable.
3. Slaughter time can be adjusted by altering the concentrates fed in the finishing period.

TABLE 5.1

Projected Weight Gains for Steers on 15-Month Grass-Cereal Beef Systems

	Daily Liveweight Gain				Cereal Feed Conversion Ratio		Cereal Feed Conversion Efficiency	
	Winter Calf		Summer Calf					
	kg/day	lb/day	kg/day	lb/day	Winter Calf	Summer Calf	Winter Calf	Summer Calf
Birth - turnout (first winter)	0.7	1.5	0.7	1.5	3.2	3.0	0.31	0.33
Grazing (spring - autumn)	0.7	1.5	0.6	1.3	-	-	-	-
Finishing winter	1.1	2.4	1.2	2.6	5.8	6.0	0.17	0.17
Overall	0.8	1.8	0.9	2.0	3.5	4.0	0.29	0.25
Concentrates fed	1.28 tonnes	1.25 tons	1.37 tonnes	1.35 tons				

During the period of grazing, daily liveweight gain is below that of cereal beef. However, following housing there is compensatory gain once cereals or concentrates are introduced.

(After Meat and Livestock Commission, 1977)

TABLE 5.2

Stocking Densities

	Winter Calf		Summer Calf	
	Beasts/ha	Beasts/acre	Beasts/ha	Beasts/acre
Turnout - mid-season	9.9	4.0	14.8	6.0
Mid-season - yarding	4.9	2.0	7.4	3.0
Overall (during grazing)	7.4	3.0	11.1	4.5

4. Useful system for farmers producing own cereal and straw.
5. The system requires lower quantities of concentrates than cereal beef.
6. The feed input costs are less than cereal beef.
7. There is a minimal need for grass conservation.
8. There is a relatively high gross margin (equivalent to 30 - 36 per cent of the total returns).
9. Quick capital turnover occurs.

Disadvantages

1. Sensitive to price of calf (15 per cent of total returns).
2. Sensitive to price of cereals (45 per cent of total returns).
3. System requires buildings.
4. Often excessive protein is fed during the finishing period. A level of 12 per cent is adequate.
5. Feed conversion efficiency must be monitored closely because over 360 kg (750 lb) it declines quickly to an average of 8.1 kg (lb) feed per kg (lb) gain. Thus timing of slaughter is important.

Veterinary Problems

1. Most problems in calf period (see page 56).
2. Mortality in calf period about 4.6 per cent.
3. Enzootic pneumonia commonly occurs.

Grazing Period

1. Parasitic gastro-enteritis.
2. Parasitic bronchitis (husk).
3. Possibly liver fluke.
4. Copper deficiency in some areas.

Finishing Period

1. Acidosis, ruminitis.
2. Occasional liver abscesses.
3. Bloat.
4. Laminitis.
5. Mortality post weaning is about 1.9 per cent (range 0 - 7.5 per cent).
6. Overall mortality is about 6.3 per cent (range 0 - 15.9 per cent).
7. Warts.
8. Ringworm.
9. Often, if insufficient bedding, the animals are dirty and soiled at slaughter.

Alternatives or Improvements to 15-Month Grass-Cereal Beef

1. The use of bulls instead of steers.
2. The incorporation of cheaper feeds, e.g. maize silage, sugar beet pulp, turnips, swedes, potatoes, dried grass.
3. Use of anabolic steroids.
4. Use of growth promoters.

18-Month Grass-Cereal Beef

The system is commonly used in cattle to allow finishing in yards during their second winter. The system allows considerable variation and flexibility according to the resources available and required time of finishing.

Type of Animal

Most types of cattle will fit into the system. Male animals (entire or castrated) and heifers can be used. All breeds can be accommodated, including late-maturing dairy-bred animals such as Friesians or Charolais, Limousin, Blonde d'Aquitaine, Simmental, or South Devon cross Friesian, and early-maturing dairy-bred crosses including Aberdeen Angus, Hereford and Murray Grey cross Friesian. Pure beef bred animals have also been reared in the system.

The System (see Table 5.3)

Calf Rearing

The calves used can be born in autumn, winter or early spring. The calves are early-weaned and then fed roughage, usually hay, although occasionally silage is used. Concentrates are offered up to a maximum of 2.25 kg (5 lbs) per day. A daily weight gain of 0.75 kg (1.7 lb) should be aimed for so that at turnout an autumn-born calf reaches a weight of 180 kg (400 lb).

Grazing Period

The land for grazing and conservation is usually divided so that to begin with the majority is used for conservation. Following turnout the animals should receive about 1.25 kg (3 lb) of concentrates for two or three weeks until they are used to grazing. A stocking density to mid-season of 8.5 beasts/hectare (3.4 beasts/acre) should be aimed for. As the appetites of the animals increase so grass growth tends to reduce. Thus towards mid-July the cattle are normally provided with extra grazing. Stocking density in the second half of the grazing season should be at 5.0 beasts/hectare (2.0 beasts/acre). Weight gains tend to decline from late August onwards and often at this stage some concentrate is provided.

Finishing Period

Once the animals are yarded they are fed grass silage and concentrates (normally barley). The amount of feed depends partly on breed and partly on proposed time of slaughter. Provided the amount and quality of the roughage are known, then the weight of cereal to be fed daily can be calculated so as to produce an animal of the required weight gain, total liveweight and time of slaughter. Average concentrate consumption figures for the winter period are 0.6 ton(nes) for Friesians and 0.4 ton(nes) for Hereford cross Friesian steers. Silage usage is of the order of 4.0 ton(nes) or 1.2 ton(nes) of hay for Friesians and for Hereford cross Friesians the consumption is about 3.0 ton(nes) of silage or 0.9 ton(nes) of hay.

Usually concentrate feeding is limited, being up to 5.5 kg (11 lb) for Friesian steers although early-maturing cattle such as Hereford cross Friesian animals will probably not require more than 2.75 kg (6 lb) daily. Animals tend to be slaughtered at a weight of 410 - 520 kg (900 - 1145 lb) when between 16 and 20 months old. The carcase produced is usually of good conformation and variable fat cover, depending on the breed used.

TABLE 5.3

Performance of Cattle in the 18-Month Grass-Cereal System

(Age at end of period)	Liveweight at End of Period		Daily Liveweight Gain During Period	
	kg	lb	kg	lb
On arrival	45	100	-	-
Calf rearing (6 months)	180	400	0.7	1.5
Summer grazing (12 months)	300	650	0.7	1.5
Second winter (18 months)	480	1060	0.8	1.8
Overall	480	1060	0.7	1.5

Stocking Rates

	Beasts/hectare	Beasts/acre
Slaughter age (days)	580	
Stocking density (beasts/hectare(acre)		
Grazing	3.1	1.2
Overall	5.1	2.0
Total fertiliser used	230 kg	200 lb
Total concentrates used	1050 kg	1 ton
Concentrate feed conversion ratio	2.6	2.6
Silage fed	4.0 tonnes	4.0 tons
Or hay	1.2 tonnes	1.2 tons

(After Meat and Livestock Commission, 1977)

Grass Silage

Conserved grass should be cut towards the end of May to ensure high digestibility or D value of between 63 and 66. The D value depends on the variety of grass grown as well as the stage when cut. Permanent pasture tends to produce less silage per hectare than leys and it is also dependent on the amount of fertiliser used.

Consumption of silage in the period is about 4 ton(nes) for Friesian steers and 3 ton(nes) for Hereford cross Friesian steers. If hay is used the corresponding weights are 1.2 ton(nes) and 0.9 ton(nes) respectively.

Buildings

Accommodation will be required for calf rearing, including calf housing of 0.9 - 1.4 m^2 (10 - 15 ft^2) and then follow-on housing of 1.4 - 2.3 m^2 (15 - 24 ft^2). Yards are necessary for the finishing period with 2.8 - 4.6 m^2 (30 - 50 ft^2) per beast, depending on size (350 - 500 kg; 770 - 1100 lb) if they are bedded or 2.0 - 2.6 m^2 (22 - 28 ft^2) if on slats. Trough space with restricted feeding is 500 - 600 mm/beast (20 - 24 ins). Water, when provided by trough, should be at an area of 2000 mm^2/beast (3.2 ins^2) or one bowl to a maximum of 15 animals.

Advantages

1. Relatively high gross margin (35 - 40 per cent of total returns).
2. Relatively low feed and forage costs (35 - 40 per cent of total returns).
3. Relatively low cost of calf compared with total returns (15 - 23 per cent).
4. A versatile system which can be used on different breeds and sexes of cattle.
5. The system can be altered according to the availability of feeding-stuffs. It can also be changed relative to likely market trends and where the performance is not as predicted.

Disadvantages

1. Bad grassland management can produce poor weight gains during grazing, particularly in the second half of the season. Thus sensible management of grass must be practised in the first part of the grazing season, with use of hay or silage after seven months and some concentrate supplementation in the period before yarding.

2. Concentrate feeding can be justified during the last month to six weeks of the grazing season to prevent poor weight gains during this period as well as to reduce costs during the winter period. An acceptable daily level of feeding in Friesian steers is about 1 - 2 kg (2 - 4.5 lb).

3. Care must be taken in the preparation and storage of the roughage used. Ideally it should be of sufficient nutritional quality to reduce the amount of concentrate fed. This means ensuring cutting hay and silage to produce high digestibility rather than bulk. The correct storage of hay to prevent spoilage and of silage to ensure that good anaerobic fermentation occurs without spoilage occurring either before or when the clamp is opened, are essential.

4. In the finishing period money can be wasted by the provision of protein supplementation of concentrate feeds. Most silage or hay diets will provide sufficient protein for finishing animals and so the concentrate need only consist of rolled barley.

5. It is important to calculate accurately the quantity of silage available for the cattle held. When this has been done the required liveweight gain can be calculated. Miscalculations can be extremely costly as at lower weight gains the finishing period will be increased and in consequence so will the amount of silage/hay consumed. Thus in Friesian steers a reduction in daily weight gain from 0.8 kg (1.8 lb) to 0.7 kg (1.5 lb) will increase the silage consumed by 1 tonne (1 ton) per animal (M.L.C. Data Sheets, 1977).

6. Despite calculations, problems may arise in obtaining the required weight gain. When these occur the decision has to be made as to whether or not to increase the amount of concentrates consumed or to sell as stores. Costings will need to be made. However, depending on the difference between prices of stores and fat cattle, it is often better to sell the animals at the required time as stores rather than completely alter the system of management.

Veterinary Problems

Most problems are again in the calf period:-

1. Bought-in calves, usually from market and/or dealer.
2. Colostrum status usually unknown.
3. Enteric problems.
4. Salmonellosis always possible.
5. Enzootic pneumonia.
6. Mortality in calf-rearing period 4.7 *per cent*.

Rearing and Finishing Period

1. Parasitic problems, especially parasitic gastro-enteritis and bronchitis. (Liver fluke to a lesser extent.)
2. Mineral deficiencies occur and are dependent on the area but include copper, cobalt, selenium (occasionally iodine).
3. Digestive upsets during introduction of the winter feeding ration.
4. Ringworm.
5. Pediculosis.
6. If there is insufficient bedding then the animals are often dirty and soiled at slaughter.
7. Mortality after calf period is 1.9 *per cent* (range 0 - 6.7 *per cent*).
8. Overall mortality is 6.1 *per cent* (range 0 - 15.4 *per cent*).

Alternatives and Improvements to 18-Month Grass-Cereal Beef

1. Use of bulls instead of steers.
2. Use of anabolic steroids.
3. Use of growth promoters.
4. Use of maize silage.
5. Use of grass silage beef (see page 81).

1. Use of Bulls

Bulls can be used in the 18-month grass-cereal system but because of safety regulations, the system is little or never used. Production benefits are shown, in that bulls consistently gain weight faster, although their stocking density at grass is less. Generally they finish slightly later than steers. Thus although the potential is there, the bull system is little used. Gross margin per head for bulls is often about 25 *per cent* higher than for steers but because of a lower stocking density the gross margin per hectare is only about 15 *per cent* higher.

TABLE 5.4

Performance of Bulls and Steers on 18-Month Grass-Cereal Beef

	Bulls		Steers	
Daily liveweight gain	kg	lb	kg	lb
Summer grazing	0.9	2.0	0.8	1.7
Winter finishing	0.9	2.0	0.8	1.7
Overall	0.9	2.0	0.8	1.7
Carcase weight	300	60	266	585
Concentrates fed (kg - tons)	1300	1.3 tons	1300	1.3 tons
Slaughter age (days)	596		579	
Stocking density (beasts/hectare/acre)	3.0	1.2	3.2	1.3

(Meat and Livestock Commission, 1977)

2. Anabolic Steroids

It is probable that most benefit is obtained during the finishing period, although implants of longer duration may be used.

3. Growth Promoters

The use of monensin sodium or bambermycin can be of help in both the grazing and finishing period to improve weight gain and feed conversion efficiency.

4. Use of Maize Silage

This is an alternative method of finishing 18-month old steers and will normally result in higher daily liveweight gains and slaughter weights than cattle on a more conventional silage and concentrates diet. Daily consumption of maize is about 23 kg (50 lb) with 0.6 kg (1.3 lb) cereals, 1.6 kg (3.5 lb) protein concentrates and 3.9 kg (8.5 lb) other feeds, mainly hay.

TABLE 5.5

Finishing 18-Month Steers (Maize Silage)

	kg	lb
Daily liveweight gain (kg/day)	0.9	2.0
Slaughter weight	493	1085
Carcase weight	271	585
Maize silage consumed (dry matter)	1.4 tonnes	1.4 tons

(Meat and Livestock Commission, 1977)

Reference

MEAT AND LIVESTOCK COMMISSION (1977) Data Sheets. Meat and Livestock Commission, Bletchley. pp. 1-72.

5. Use of Grass Silage Beef

The system is really an alternative to 18-month grass-cereal beef. The cattle do not graze at all but remain housed throughout their lives. Roughage is provided throughout the year in the form of silage and the concentrate in the growing period is usually in the form of rolled barley. Stocking rates in terms of cattle per hectare (acre) can be maintained at a very high level, and the number of cattle which can be kept on the system can easily be calculated on the basis of building and land availability plus the yield of grass. There is no wastage as can occur with grazing due to the grass outgrowing the animals' appetites, and there is less poaching.

Type of Animal

Dairy-bred animals.

Advantages

1. There is maximum utilisation of grassland.
2. Bulls can be used in a system with grass without the problem of providing adequate safety fencing, etc.
3. There is a high gross margin per hectare (acre).
4. Relatively high gross margin overall.
5. Buildings are fully utilised throughout the year.
6. Endoparasitic problems are virtually eliminated.
7. Poaching is minimised.
8. The system can be altered according to availability of feed, etc.

Disadvantages

1. Adequate buildings are required.
2. Sufficient storage capacity must be available for the silage.
3. Some farms may be tempted to use protein supplementation of concentrate feeds in the finishing period which is unnecessary.
4. Care must be taken in silage making.

Veterinary Problems

Most problems occur in the calf unit.

1. Bought-in calves, usually from market and/or dealer.
2. Colostrum status is unknown.
3. Enteric problems.

4. Salmonellosis possible.

5. Enzootic pneumonia.

6. Mortality in calf rearing period about five per cent.

Rearing and Finishing Period

1. Digestive upsets.

2. Ringworm.

3. Pediculosis.

4. Animals may be very soiled if insufficient bedding is provided prior to slaughter.

5. Mortality about three per cent (range 0 - 13 per cent).

6. Overall mortality about six per cent.

Improvements

1. Use of anabolic steroids in steers.

2. Use of bulls (see Table 5.6).

TABLE 5.6

Grass Silage Bull Beef Performance Results

	kg	lb
Daily liveweight gain from 3 months	1.0	2.2
Slaughter weight	470	1035
Stocking rate	6.2/ha	2.5/acre
Slaughter age (months)	16.5	
Silage (tonnes DM)	5.5	5.5
Barley	840	1850

24-Month Grass-Cereal Beef

Type of Animal

The animals used are dairy-bred calves. The system can be adapted for both early and late-maturing calves but it is of more use for Aberdeen Angus cross Friesian or Hereford cross Friesian than Friesian. Heifers can be used satisfactorily in the system. Steers of late-maturing breeds will probably not obtain sufficient fat cover unless concentrates are fed in the second grazing season.

The System (see Table 5.7)

Calf Rearing

The calves are born in the spring, they are early-weaned and then fed hay and concentrates until turnout in early summer.

First Grazing Season

The calves graze for about four months until the autumn. They are about seven months old when housed and weigh about 180 kg (400 lbs).

Second Winter Housing

The animals are yarded for about six months, during which they usually receive silage plus a small amount of concentrates (e.g. rolled barley).

Second Grazing Season

The animals return to grass during the early spring. They may receive small quantities of cereals after turnout. During the summer, weight gain should be at a level of 0.8 kg (1.8 lb). In order to ensure adequate weight gains in the autumn, small amounts of cereal should be supplied from late August.

Third Winter Housing

The animals are yarded when about 19 months old and during the finishing winter the cattle receive silage and concentrates. The aim is to keep down the amount of cereal fed. The cattle are slaughtered at about 20 to 24 months old, when weighing 525 kg (1155 lb) with a carcase weight of 270 kg (595 lb).

Buildings

Specialised accommodation will be required for calves. Usually as the animals are young at turnout a space of 0.9 - 1.4 m^2 (10 - 15 ft^2) is all that is necessary. Yards are needed for cattle in their second and third winters. However, many of the older animals will be slaughtered as they reach two years old and so potential crowding problems will be relieved. Straw yard areas of 1.9 - 4.0 m^2 (20 - 43 ft^2) and 4.0 - 4.6 m^2 (43 - 50 ft^2) are required in the second and third winters respectively, or if slats are used, the area in the second winter is 1.4 - 2.3 m^2 (15 - 25 ft^2) and 1.9 - 2.6 m^2 (20 - 28 ft^2) in the third housing period. Trough space should be at least 500 mm (20 ins) in the

TABLE 5. 7

Performance Characteristics of 24-Month Grass-Cereal Beef

	Liveweight at End of Period		Daily Liveweight Gain During Period	
(Age at end of period)	kg	lb	kg	lb
At arrival	40	88	-	-
Calf rearing (3 months)	100	220	0.7	1.5
First grazing season (7 months)	180	396	0.6	1.3
Second winter housing (13 months)	260	572	0.5	1.1
Second grazing period (19 months)	400	880	0.8	1.8
Third winter housing (24 months)	525	1155	0.8	1.8
Overall	525	1155	0.7	1.5

Stocking Rates

	Beasts/hectare	Beasts/acre
First grazing season	2.5	1.0
Second grazing season	10.0	4.0
Overall	4.7	1.7
Total fertiliser/hectare(acre)	210 kg	185 lb
Total concentrates used	1.1 tonnes	1.1 tons
Concentrates/head/day (third winter)	3 kg	6.5 lb
Concentrate feed conversion ratio (third winter)	3.7	3.7
Overall	2.5	2.5

(Sources various; mainly Meat and Livestock Commission)

second winter and 600 mm (24 ins) in the third winter. Water bowls should be provided at a maximum of one per 15 beasts in the second winter and one per 12 animals in the third winter. If water troughs are used a minimum of 2000 mm^2 (3.2 in^2) should be available per animal.

Advantages

1. A high gross margin (about 37 - 45 per cent of gross returns).
2. Relatively low feed/forage costs (about 36 - 40 per cent of gross returns).
3. Relatively low cost of calf (13 - 20 per cent of gross returns).
4. The system can be altered to accommodate different breeds and sexes of cattle.
5. The system allows good utilisation of home-produced feedingstuffs.

Disadvantages

1. There is a slow turnover of capital.
2. There is a high capital requirement before a return.
3. There are often poor growth rates at grass towards the end of the first grazing season.

Veterinary Problems

Problems mainly occur in the calf period:

1. Calves are mainly bought in from market or dealers.
2. Colostrum status variable.
3. Enteric conditions.
4. Salmonellosis.
5. Enzootic pneumonia is often a severe problem.
6. Mortality in calf period about 4.7 per cent.

Rearing and Finishing Period

1. Parasitic gastro-enteritis, parasitic bronchitis and liver fluke.
2. Nutritional deficiencies, particularly copper, cobalt, selenium.
3. If insufficient bedding the animals are often soiled and dirty at slaughter.
4. Mortality overall 6.2 per cent (range 0 - 15.1 per cent).
5. Mortality in weaned calf 1.9 per cent (range 0 - 6.6 per cent).

Developments or Improvements to 24-Month Grass-Cereal Beef

1. Use of growth promoters can assist in all stages of production.
2. Use of anabolic steroids, particularly in the finishing period, may be of help.

20-Month Grass Beef

The production system is designed to make maximum use of grass in the production process. The animals are finished off grass and the aim is to finish them without the need for concentrates.

Type of Animals

As animals are to be finished on a grass diet the cattle best suited to this are early-maturing breeds such as Aberdeen Angus cross Friesians or Hereford cross Friesians, although Friesians can be reared in the system. Heifers can be utilised as well as steers.

The System (see Table 5.8)

Calf Rearing

Calves from the dairy herd are bought in January to April. Ideally they are born as early in the year as possible so as to ensure early turnout. The calves are early-weaned and are turned out in the spring when about 12 weeks old. Calves born in the early spring are turned out as soon as is practicable. Daily liveweight gain during the initial period should be 0.7 kg (1.5 lb).

First Grazing Period

The animals graze all summer and the aim is for them to gain about 0.7 kg (1.5 lb) daily. Growth is aided by the feeding of supplementary barley during the grazing period. The cattle enter yards in the autumn.

Second Winter Period

In the winter they are fed silage or good quality hay so as to gain 0.5 - 0.6 kg (1.1 - 1.3 lb) daily. Weight gain is aided by provision of about 1.5 kg (3 lb) concentrates daily. The animals reach the following spring in a well-grown state but with little fat cover. An average of 2.5 ton(nes) of silage are consumed in the winter period although this varies from 2.25 - 3 ton(nes), depending on breed, duration of period, etc.

Second Grazing Season

The animals at turnout are fit and lean and gain about 1.0 kg (2.2 lb) a day until slaughtered. This increase in weight is helped by compensatory gain and the use of good grassland management. Small amounts of concentrates may be required at the start of the grazing season. The animals are slaughtered off grass between July and September, weighing 430 - 510 kg (950 - 1125 lb). Carcases tend to be of 230 - 270 kg (505 - 595 lb) with a moderate fat cover and medium to good quality carcase. Friesians tend to be slaughtered at 500 kg (1100 lb) whereas Hereford cross Friesians are killed about 50 kg (110 lb) lighter.

Buildings

Specialist calf housing is required. Depending on the age at turnout there is a need for calf rearing space of 0.9 - 1.4 m^2 (10 - 15 ft^2) and follow-on accommodation of 1.4 - 1.9 m^2 (15 - 20 ft^2). The grazing animals also require accommodation, usually in yards, for their second winter period. If straw yards are used an area of 4.0 - 4.6 m^2

TABLE 5.8

Performance Characteristics of 20-Month Grass Beef

	Liveweight at End of Period		Daily Liveweight Gain During Period	
	kg	lb	kg	lb
(Age at end of period)				
At arrival	44	96	-	-
Calf rearing (4 months)	135	295	0.7	1.5
First grazing season (8 months)	219	480	0.7	1.5
Second winter housing (14 months)	335	737	0.6	1.3
Second grazing period (20 months)	490	1075	0.9	2.0
Overall	490	1075	0.7	1.5

Stocking Rates

	Beasts/hectare	Beasts/acre
First grazing season	3.5	1.4
Second grazing season	3.0	1.2
First grazing season + winter	3.0	1.2
Second grazing season + winter	2.5	1.0
Total fertiliser	210 kg	185 lb
Total concentrates used	0.9 tonnes	0.9 tons
Concentrate feed conversion ratio	2.0	2.0

(Sources various: mainly Meat and Livestock Commission, 1977)

(43 - 50 ft^2) is necessary or 1.9 - 2.6 m^2 (20 - 28 ft^2) for slats. Trough space when restricted is about 600 mm (24 ins) per beast. Water bowls should be provided at a level of one to a maximum of 15 beasts with 2000 mm^2 (3.2 ins^2) trough space per animal.

Advantages

1. A high gross margin (43 - 46 per cent of gross returns).
2. Relatively low feed/forage costs (32 - 35 per cent of gross returns).
3. Relatively low calf costs (14 - 18 per cent of gross returns).
4. There is good utilisation of grazing and forage conservation is kept low despite the age of the animals at slaughter.
5. The system can be used for different breeds and sexes, although its use for late-maturing breeds requires significant concentrate feeding in the second grazing season.

Disadvantages

1. Poor weight gains of calves may occur in the first grazing season if the calves are born towards the spring.
2. If excess concentrates are fed in the second winter period then costs rise and also compensatory gain tends to be less when the animals are turned out in the spring.
3. Capital investment in the system tends to be tied up for a long period without there being any return.
4. There is a high capital requirement before a return occurs.

Veterinary Problems

Disease mainly occurs during the calf period:

1. Calves tend to be bought in, i.e. dealer or market calves.
2. Colostrum status tends to be variable.
3. Enteric conditions.
4. Salmonellosis.
5. Enzootic pneumonia is often high unless housing is good.
6. Mortality in the calf period is about 4.4 per cent.

Rearing and Finishing Periods

1. Problems are often parasitic in nature, e.g. parasitic gastroenteritis, parasitic bronchitis and, in some areas, liver fluke.
2. Nutritional deficiencies occur, particularly of copper, cobalt and selenium.
3. Mortality overall 6.1 per cent (range 0 - 14.1 per cent).
4. Mortality in post-weaning period 1.8 per cent (range 0 - 6.9 per cent).

Alternatives or Improvements to 20-Month Grass Beef

1. The system can be integrated with others on the farm so as to improve the utilization of farm resources. Grazing systems can be devised to incorporate both beef and sheep production.
2. The system lends itself well to the leader/follower grazing programme. Thus the calves in their first grazing season graze paddocks prior to the older and heavier finishing cattle. (See Growing Cattle Management and Disease Notes - Part II.)
3. Growth promoters can be used throughout the whole system.
4. The use of anabolic steroids with activity over a long period may be helpful.

Reference

MEAT AND LIVESTOCK COMMISSION (1977) Data Sheets. Meat and Livestock Commission, Bletchley. pp. 1-72.

24-Month Grass Beef

Like the 20-month grass beef system, this makes maximum use of grass. The animals are slaughtered off grass with the aim being to reduce the amount of concentrates fed in the production system.

Type of Animals

The animals again are to be finished off grass and so the system is most suitable for early-maturing cattle such as Aberdeen Angus cross Friesians or Hereford cross Friesians. Friesians can be successfully used in the system provided they finish by early autumn. Heifers, as well as steers, can be satisfactorily used.

The System (see Table 5.9)

Calf Rearing

Calves used are born in the autumn between September and December. The animals are early-weaned and are turned out to grass in the early spring when 4 to 7 months old. Daily liveweight gain in the initial period is 0.7 kg (1.5 lb).

First Grazing Period

During the first summer grazing the aim is a daily liveweight gain of 0.7 kg (1.5 lb). The cattle are yarded in the autumn.

Second Winter Period

During the winter they are fed silage or good quality hay at 0.5 - 0.6 kg (1.1 - 1.3 lb) daily. Weight gain is aided by the provision of up to 1.5 kg (3 lb) concentrates daily. The animals reach turnout the following spring well-grown but lean with only limited fat cover. An average of 3.25 ton(nes) of silage are consumed in the winter, but this varies between 3.0 and 3.5 ton(nes), depending on the breed and duration of the period, etc.

Second Grazing Period

At the start of the finishing period the animals are fit but not fat and gain about 0.4 kg (2 lb) a day. The weight gain is helped by compensatory gain and the use of good grassland management. The animals are slaughtered off grass from August onwards when about 24 months old and weighing 430 - 530 kg (950 - 1165 lb). The carcases tend to weigh 230 - 290 kg (505 - 640 lb) with a moderate fat cover and medium to good quality carcases. The Friesian steers tend to be slaughtered at around 525 kg (1155 lb) with Hereford cross Friesian being about 50 kg (110 lb) lighter.

Buildings

Calf housing is required, but as the animals will be about six months old at turnout, follow-on accommodation is required for the winter period. A minimum level of 1.1 - 1.9 m^2 (12 - 20 ft^2) is needed if bedding is used or 0.9 - 1.4 m^2 (10 - 15 ft^2) if on slats. During the second winter,

TABLE 5.9

Performance Characteristics of 24-Month Grass Beef

	Liveweight at End of Period		Daily Liveweight Gain During Period	
(Age at end of period)	kg	lb	kg	lb
At arrival	43	93	-	-
Calf rearing (7 months)	168	370	0.7	1.5
First grazing season (12 months)	300	660	0.7	1.5
Second winter housing (18 months)	395	870	0.5	1.1
Second grazing period (24 months)	500	1100	0.9	2.0
Overall	500	1100	0.7	1.5

Stocking Rates

	Beasts/hectare	Beasts/acre
First grazing season	6.3	2.5
Second grazing season	3.0	1.2
Overall grazing seasons and winters	2.5	1.0
Total fertilizer used	210 kg	185 lb
Total concentrates used	1 tonne	1 ton
Concentrate feed conversion ratio	2.0	2.0

(Sources various: mainly Meat and Livestock Commission, 1977)

housing is usually in the form of yards with a minimum area of 1.9 - 4.0 m^2 (20 - 43 ft^2) for slats. The minimum trough space should be 500 mm (20 in) with a water bowl per 15 cattle or 2000 mm^2 (3.2 in^2) of water trough per beast.

Advantages

1. A high gross margin is produced (44 - 48 per cent of gross returns).
2. There are relatively low feed/forage costs (35 - 41 per cent of gross returns).
3. Calf costs are quite low (10 - 15 per cent of gross returns).
4. The system is very useful for early-maturing breeds and heifers.
5. There is good utilisation of grazing.

Disadvantages

1. Poor weight gains may occur in the first grazing season.
2. If excess concentrates are fed in the second winter period then costs rise and compensatory gain tends to be less when the animals are turned out in the spring.
3. Capital investment in the system tends to be tied up for a long period without there being a return.
4. There is a high capital requirement before a return occurs.

Veterinary Problems

Most disease occurs during the initial housing period.

1. Calves are usually bought-in, i.e. from market or dealer.
2. The colostrum status is usually unknown.
3. Enteric conditions.
4. Salmonellosis.
5. Enzootic pneumonia tends to be a severe problem as there is a long initial housing period embracing both the autumn and spring peaks of disease.
6. Mortality in the calf period is 4.4 per cent.

Rearing and Finishing Periods

1. Problems of parasitic infestation often occur, e.g. parasitic gastro-enteritis and parasitic bronchitis (husk). In some areas liver fluke may be important.
2. Nutritional deficiencies occur including cobalt, selenium and copper.
3. Mortality overall is 6.2 per cent (range 0 - 13.8 per cent).
4. Mortality in the post-weaning period is 1.7 per cent (range 0 - 6.7 per cent).

Alternatives or Improvements to 24-Month Grass Beef

1. The system can be incorporated with others on the farm in order to allow improved use of the farm resources. Systems can be used to include both cattle and sheep grazing.
2. The system is ideal for using the leader/follower grazing programme. Thus the calves in the first grazing season graze paddocks prior to the older and heavier finishing cattle. (See Growing Cattle Management and Disease Notes - Part II.)
3. Growth promoters can be used throughout the whole system.
4. The use of anabolic steroids with activity over a long period may be beneficial.

Purchase of Animals

In the beef systems described, most calves are bought either from a market dealer or from a calf group at about a week old. However, there are other methods of purchase.

Purchase of Weaned Calves

Such calves are normally bought at 12 weeks old. The advantage of this is that the very critical period of calf rearing is avoided and so the disease conditions and mortality of the period do not occur. Additionally, no specialised equipment or buildings for calf rearing are required when older animals are bought. Another advantage is that the specialist labour required for successful calf rearing is unnecessary. Thus in a beef production enterprise which forms part of a larger farm mainly concentrating on cereal production, purchase of weaned calves can prevent many problems which might otherwise occur.

Reference

MEAT AND LIVESTOCK COMMISSION (1977) Data Sheets. Meat and Livestock Commission, Bletchley. pp. 1-72.

CHAPTER 6

SUCKLED CALF PRODUCTION

The system has been mentioned in "Calf Management and Disease Notes". There are many variations in production methods, dependent on the time of year born:

Autumn
Winter/spring
Summer,

and the type of region where born:

Hill
Upland
Lowland.

The systems are usually aimed at producing a calf for the autumn sales. Although the enterprise may be the main source of revenue for the farm, it integrates well with other livestock enterprises, e.g. dairy farming, sheep production, as well as acting as a brake crop and utilising waste or by-products on arable farms.

Type of Animal

Usually a beef sire which colour-marks the calves is used such as Aberdeen Angus, Charolais, Hereford, Simmental (most calves) are used, although other breeds can be kept, e.g. Blonde d'Aquitaine, Limousin and Murray Grey. The Aberdeen Angus and Murray Grey are particularly used in heifers. Although large calves grow faster, the use of bulls of the large beef breeds such as the Charolais, South Devon, and Simmental tend to increase problems of dystokia, and calving under such circumstances requires much more supervision. The cows can be of varying type but often they are crossbred and they may include Hereford cross Friesian or the Blue Grey (White Shorthorn cross Galloway).

The System (see Tables 6.1; 6.3)

Autumn-Born (August - October)

The calves will usually be born outside or soon after housing. The cow must be provided with enough feed to produce milk for the calf. The calves should have a creep area where there is access to good quality hay and concentrates. In the spring calves and dams should be turned out onto good quality grazing. Some farmers wean at this time while others wait until July. On hill and upland farms the better quality grazing and flatter areas may be required for conservation and so the grass available for the calves may be more marginal.

The calves will start grazing immediately and should be able to grow well at a time when their appetite is much greater than the milk production of the dam. During the second half of the grazing season, herbage quality declines and this is reflected in the performance of the calf. In most instances the provision of creep feed concentrates for the calves prior to weaning will help to increase their weaning weights. Provision of 2 kg (2.2 lb) a day for one-and-a-half months prior to weaning increases the weaning weight by about 23 kg (50 lb). The calves may be finished out of yards during the following winter and spring or they may be stored during this period to finish off grass. Most, however, tend to be sold at weaning at the autumn calf sales.

Winter/Spring-Born (November - April)

These calves are born inside or soon after turnout. The calf will not start grazing in any quantity until early summer. Creep feeding at grass will be little used in the early grazing season and its provision prior to weaning need only be for a few weeks. Weaning usually occurs in September to October for winter-born calves and October to November for spring-born animals. The provision of about 2 kg (4.4 lb) concentrates daily for the last 3 to 4 weeks will increase the weaning weight by about 15 kg (33 lb). These calves may be finished as lightweight cattle out of yards during the late spring or early summer, but more are stored during the winter for finishing at grass the following summer and autumn. Many of the heavy cattle tend to be sold following weaning during the autumn suckler sales. Those too light for sale are often yarded during the winter and sold as stores in the spring.

Summer-Born (May - July)

These calves are born outside and so there is limited disease risk. Feed costs tend to be low as most of the lactation takes place while the cows are at grass. They come inside with their dams and will need to have a creep area which will provide good quality hay or concentrates. The quantity of concentrate should be restricted, otherwise weight gain will be reduced at grass. Often the calves are weaned at turnout and, whether or not this is so, grass will be the main source of feed in the spring period. The provision of creep feeding towards the autumn will help increase weight at sale. Weaning often occurs in December to February and the heaviest animals may be finished in yards in early summer. Others are more likely to be finished at grass during the late summer or autumn. In many cases the yearling cattle will be sold in the autumn store sales for finishing in yards during their second winter.

Buildings

The cattle are usually housed in yards during the autumn and winter. The basic requirements vary according to the type of flooring available. Usually suckler cows are bedded on straw and a minimum bedded area per beast of 6.0 - 8.4 m^2 (65 - 90 ft^2) is required. About one ton(ne) of straw will be needed for bedding for each cow and calf if loose-housed. Dry cows require at least 3.5 m^2 (38 ft^2) per animal. Over 1 m^3 (35 ft^3) of dung will be produced by each cow monthly. Cows in a cubicle system require 3.7 - 4.2 m^2 (40 - 45 ft^2) per cow plus a creep area. The creep area will depend on the age of the calf and therefore its size but a figure of about 1.2 m^2 (13 ft^2) is usually sufficient. When cubicles are used for cows, about 150 kg (330 lb) straw or 100 kg (220 lb) shavings will be required annually. Where feed is restricted, a trough length of 600 mm (24 in) per cow is necessary. If self-feed silage is used then 150 - 300 mm (6 - 12 in) of silage face should be provided for each cow. The space allowances should, however, be as generous as possible, particularly where bulls are to be run with the cows during the winter period.

It should always be remembered in autumn-calving herds to provide enough accommodation for both cow and calf. Calves will require a creep area of about 1.0 - 1.4 m^2 (11 - 15 ft^2) per calf. The opening to the creeps should be made adjustable so that the smallest cows cannot enter this area, although the largest calves can. Where there is little difference in size between some cows and calves it may be necessary to allow access to the creep at varying intervals throughout the day by a stockman. At other times entrance to the area should be barred by a gate.

When cows are calving outside or late in the housing period so that the calves are small at turnout, the space allowances can be slightly reduced. In recent years some suckler herds have been successfully housed on slats with the slurry passing into a cellar. In such cases the space allowance per cow can be reduced to 3.3 - 4.2 m^2 (35 - 45 ft^2) although the creep area should have a solid floor and will again need to be 1.0 - 1.4 m^2 (11 - 15 ft^2) per calf. Under the Welfare Codes (MAFF, DAFS, WOAD, 1983) it is now stated that cows should not be kept on totally slatted floors (paragraph 12). This does not qualify whether it is for both dairy and beef cattle although later on dairy cows are specifically mentioned. One point which should never be neglected, although often forgotten, is that calving boxes should always be available for difficult parturitions.

Advantages

1. The system integrates well with other enterprises on farms such as arable crops, dairy cows, sheep, etc.
2. Cattle can be kept under very different conditions, e.g. hillsides where otherwise only sheep could be grazed.
3. The versatility of the system allows many feeding systems to be used in the winter, including making maximum use of by-products.

TABLE 6.1

Suckler Cow Targets

	LOWLAND		UPLAND		HILL	
	Autumn	Winter/ Spring	Autumn	Winter/ Spring	Autumn	Winter/ Spring
Calving spread (days)	100	60	100	60	100	60
Barren cows (%)	3	2	4	3	5	4
Calf mortality (%)	3	2	4	3	5	4
Calves weaned per 100 cows	95	96	92	94	91	93
Calves/cow lifetime	5.7		5.5		5.4	

(Meat and Livestock Commission, 1977)

Disadvantages

1. The profitability of the system fluctuates markedly and is dependent on the requirement of suckled calves during the autumn sales. This partly depends on the availability of calves, but is affected more by the financial status of the beef industry at that particular time.
2. Attention has to be paid to the cost of feed during the winter period. This amounts to about 15 to 35 per cent of gross returns, or half the variable costs. It is therefore essential that winter feeds are of good quality and fed correctly.

3. There can be poor fertility with a high percentage of barren animals.
4. Mortality of calves can be high so that calves reared per 100 cows is often well below the performance target.
5. The calving spread is often very wide, which makes it difficult to successfully manage the cow and her offspring.

Veterinary Problems

Calves

1. Coli-septicaemia.
2. Viral diarrhoea.
3. Coccidiosis/cryptosporidiosis.
4. Mortality of calves is often high.
5. Infectious bovine rhinotracheitis.
6. Other respiratory infections including *Pasteurella* spp.
7. Parasitic gastroenteritis may occur, particularly in autumn-born calves.
8. Parasitic bronchitis (husk) can occur, particularly in autumn-born calves.
9. Hypomagnesaemia.
10. Copper deficiency.
11. Selenium deficiency.

Cows

1. Fertility is usually not as good as indicated by the cows producing one calf annually. Calving spread in a herd is often very wide, being up to six months (conception rate 30 *per cent* and above). Ideally calvings should be over as short a period as possible, e.g. 2 to 3 months (70 to 60 *per cent* conception rate).
2. Barren cow numbers are often high. Average numbers tend to be;

TABLE 6.2 Percentage of Barren Cows

	Autumn	Winter/Spring
Lowland	7.5	5.5
Upland	4.7	6.6
Hill	6.2	6.2

(Meat and Livestock Commission, 1977).

3. Hypomagnesaemia.
4. Copper deficiency.

TABLE 6.3

Acceptable Performance Levels for Suckled Calves

	LOWLAND		UPLAND		HILL	
	Autumn	Winter/Spring	Autumn	Winter/Spring	Autumn	Winter/Spring
Gain (kg/day)	0.9	1.0	0.85	0.95	0.8	0.7
Gain (lb/day)	2.0	2.2	1.9	2.1	1.8	1.5
Weaning weight (kg)	320	250	295	240	280	230
Weaning weight (lb)	705	550	650	530	615	505
Stocking rate (cows/ hectare)	2.0	2.3	1.5	1.8	0.9	1.0
Stocking rate (cows/ acre)	0.8	0.9	0.6	0.7	0.4	0.4
Concentrates per cow and calf unit (tonnes)	0.3	0.3	0.3	0.3	0.25	0.25

(Source: Meat and Livestock Commission, 1977)

Alternatives and Improvements to Suckled Calf Production

1. Bull Beef Production

Bull calves are traditionally castrated to prevent problems caused by rearing calves of both sexes together. Bull calves over five months old may cause problems with increased riding and the possibility of heifer calves becoming pregnant. There is less of a problem with the cows as most should be in calf by the time the bull calves are reaching puberty. However, problems can arise if the cows have a very wide calving spread. The bull calves tend to grow faster (about 10 *per cent*) and are heavier (about seven *per cent*) at weaning than steers of similar age and breeding. Entires thereby improve the gross margin per cow by about six *per cent* and gross margin per hectare (acre) by four *per cent*.

TABLE 6.4

Performance of Bull and Steer Suckled Calves

	Bulls		Steers	
	kg	lb	kg	lb
Daily liveweight gain	1.0	2.2	0.9	2.0
Weaning weight	291	640	272	600

(Meat and Livestock Commission, 1977)

2. Oestrous synchronisation techniques can be employed to ensure a tighter calving pattern and thereby improve the ease of management. Both prostaglandin injection and the use of progesterone-impregnated intravaginal devices have proved successful.

3. The use of artificial insemination can be of value with oestrous synchronisation techniques. This allows the use of a different breed to the animals already on the farm or the use of sires of superior breeding.

4. Condition scoring can ensure animals are in the correct condition at the time of service and calving. Cows should be at a condition score of 2 to 3 at service.

5. Double-suckling of autumn and winter suckler cows can produce extra gross margins per cow but this does depend on the ability of the cow to produce sufficient milk for both calves. There is also often a problem in getting the cow to accept the second calf. This can be overcome by introducing the calf at birth and ensuring that the introduced calf has some of the foetal fluid and placenta rubbed over it. Otherwise, placing a strong-smelling scent on both calves may be of help, or the spraying of the cow herself may assist.

TABLE 6.5

Targets for Double-Suckling Beef

Calves reared per cow	1.9	
Daily liveweight gain of calf	0.9 kg	2.0 lb
Total weaning weight	450 kg	990 lb
Stocking rate, cows	1.5/hectare	0.6/acre

(Meat and Livestock Commission, 1977)

6. Multiple Suckling

This usually involves good milking cows, mostly of dairy origin. The majority of cows are surplus to dairy herd requirements but some herds going out of milk production subsequently use the cows for multiple suckling. Usually dairy cows adopt calves more easily than with the beef breeds. To obtain high returns, cows must produce adequate milk to rear 10 to 12 calves per year. Calves are weaned at 5 to 12 weeks old. The system does require labour to ensure successful adoption of the calves by the cow, but subsequently the amount of supervision is considerably less than for bucket-fed calves. Introduction of new batches of calves can lead to infection among them.

Each calf should receive 4 to 6 litres (7 to 10 pints) of milk either in two or three feeds daily. Often the calves are housed but the cows go out to pasture during the day and the cow is introduced to the calves twice daily. During the first month it is often recommended that the calves are tied up or single-penned before sucking the cow, to prevent them sucking each other. In some herds, once the calves are successfully introduced to the cow, the group can be turned out to grass. Whether inside or outdoors, provision of a creep with concentrate and hay should be ensured from a few days old if early-weaning is contemplated.

One method of using the system is to have each batch on the cow between two and three months, the first batch consisting of four calves, the second of three calves and the third of two calves. Some farmers turn out the calves with the cows and then allow a free-for-all so as to reduce labour. The aim is for the ability of cows to reject the calves, when attached by a large number of hungry calves attempting to suck them, to be reduced. Any particularly antagonistic cow which does not allow sucking will develop an udder very distended with milk. The swelling will cause the animal considerable discomfort and so usually the cow will allow the calves to relieve her by sucking.

TABLE 6.6

Mortality in Suckler Herds

(Home-Reared Calves)

	% Born Dead or Died within 48 hours		% Calves Died from Birth to Weaning (6-10 Months)	
	Average	90% Range	Average	90% Range
Lowland				
Autumn	3.9	0 - 12.1	1.9	0 - 5.9
Winter/Spring	3.4	0 - 11.4	1.6	0 - 4.8
Upland				
Autumn	3.8	0 - 13.3	2.1	0 - 6.3
Winter/Spring	3.2	0 - 11.0	1.7	0 - 5.4
Hill				
Autumn	4.0	0 - 14.7	2.4	0 - 7.7
Winter/Spring	3.3	0 - 11.8	1.9	0 - 6.9

(Source: Meat and Livestock Commission, 1976)

Suckled Calves

The calves produced in suckler herds have a variable life span following weaning. Some of the possible destinations are shown in Figure 6.1.

FIGURE 6.1 Suckled Calves - Destinations

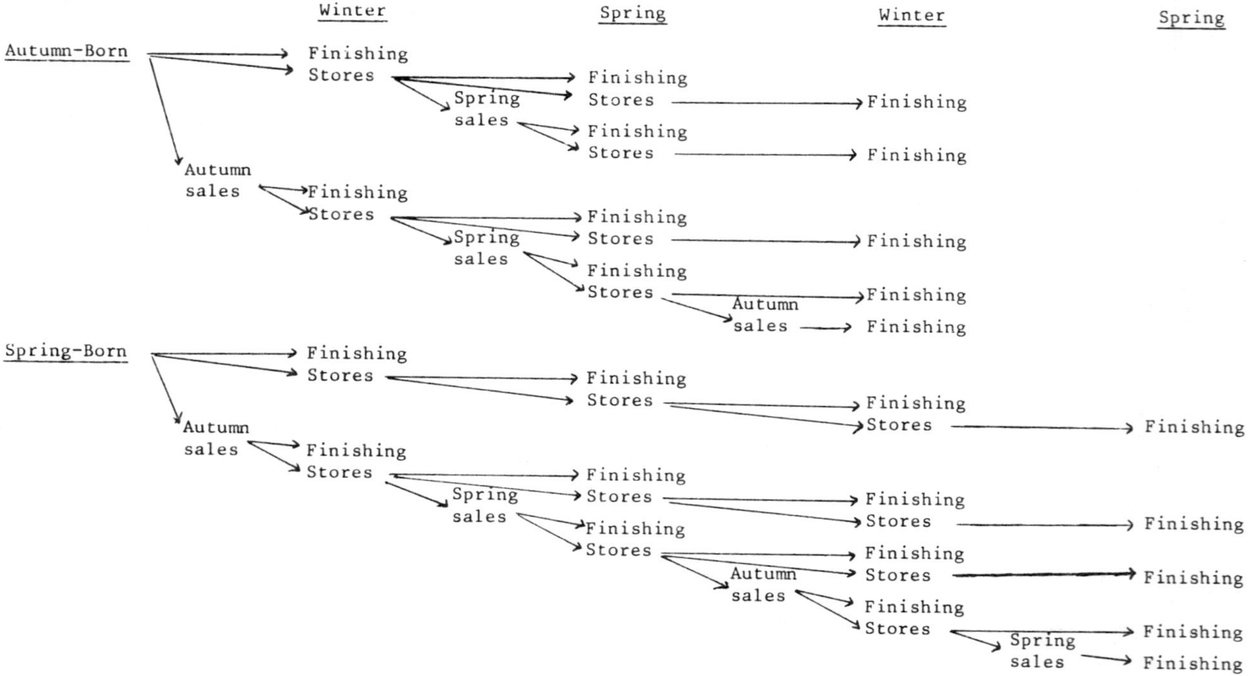

Pedigree Beef Herds

Most of these are run on similar lines to suckler cow herds. The aim is to produce cattle of acceptable size and conformation for sale privately or at pedigree sales. Calves are registered with the appropriate Breed Society. Some of the beef breed cows have a poor ability to milk so that nurse cows are sometimes used to ensure the rapid, sustained growth of calves. The use of such cows is becoming less common because of a reduced income from most pedigree animal sales compared with a few years ago. Attention has, therefore, been drawn to the milking qualities of the beef breeds. Normally, bull and heifer calves and their dams are run together for six months, but often after this time the sexes are segregated. Bulls and heifers may be examined by a breeder panel for conformation and size, and in some breeds, veterinary inspections may take place.

References

MEAT AND LIVESTOCK COMMISSION (1976) Cattle Facts: A Manual of Economic Standards. Meat and Livestock Commission, Bletchley. pp. 1-132.

MEAT AND LIVESTOCK COMMISSION (1977) Data Sheets. Meat and Livestock Commission, Bletchley. pp. 1-72.

MINISTRY OF AGRICULTURE, FISHERIES AND FOOD/DEPARTMENT OF AGRICULTURE AND FISHERIES FOR SCOTLAND/WELSH OFFICE AGRICULTURAL DEPARTMENT (1983) Codes of Recommendations for the Welfare of Livestock - Cattle. Leaflet 701. pp. 1-16.

CHAPTER 7

SYSTEMS FOR PURCHASED STORES AND SUCKLED CALVES

SEMI-INTENSIVE

Overwintering of Suckled Calves

Animals of varying type are used and the system allows maximum use of home-produced feeds. The usual aim of overwintering is to keep the animals growing. The feeding is suitable to include a high proportion of by-products and the aim is to provide a minimum of cereal or concentrates.

Type of Animals

Most spring-born calves are too light to be finished during the following winter period. Some autumn-born calves are also not heavy enough to be finished during the winter housing period. Other heavier calves are kept on high-roughage diets to be finished at a heavier weight off grass the following summer.

The System (see Table 7.1)

Following purchase, the animals are housed and fed sparingly to produce a daily gain of 0.4 - 0.6 kg (0.9 - 1.3 lb). The housed period normally lasts for five to six months. The rate of gain will depend on the future destination of the animals. If the animals are to be finished on the same farm then a gain of 0.4 kg (0.9 lb) daily is satisfactory as it allows the animals to be fit but not fat at turnout in the spring and so make maximum use of compensatory gain. Also, there are breed differences and early-maturing crosses should be reared to gain at the 0.4 kg (0.9 lb) per day level. If the cattle are to be sold in the spring then the animals must not look too thin and a gain of 0.6 kg (1.3 lb) is advisable. Late-maturing crosses will also need to be reared at the higher level of 0.6 kg (1.3 lb) daily.

Buildings

Usually the animals are housed in yards on straw with a space allowance per beast of 1.9 - 4.0 m^2 (20 - 43 ft^2) and a trough length with restricted feeding of 500 mm (20 in) per animal. If animals are kept on slats the space allowance can be reduced to 1.4 - 2.3 m^2 (15 - 25 ft^2). One water bowl should be provided for a maximum of 15 animals or a water trough space of 2000 mm^2 (3.2 in) per animal is necessary.

TABLE 7.1

Overwintering of Suckled Calves - Results

	kg	lb
Feeding period (days)	160	
Daily gain	0.4	0.8
Starting weight	234	515
Weight at sale	292	643
Concentrate usage	235	515

(Sources various - including Meat and Livestock Commission)

Advantages

1. The animals are kept for only a limited period (five or six months) before a return on capital is obtained.
2. Provided animals are bought at a low price and sold at the right time in the spring, an acceptable gross margin is obtained (about 20 *per cent* of gross returns is gained in good years).
3. It can make use of arable waste or by-products, or other waste feeds.
4. Limited labour is required in the system, and is of a non-specialised nature.

Disadvantages

1. The animals can be bought dearly and sold cheaply in the spring. This can lead to a negative gross margin. It is therefore essential to buy and sell animals at the right price.
2. The cost of the calf is relatively high (usually over 50 *per cent* of the gross returns - occasionally up to 90 *per cent* when negative gross margins occur).
3. The cost of feed is high (usually over 15 to 25 *per cent* of the gross returns). The concentrate costs amount to over half the feed costs.
4. Often too much concentrate is fed in the overwinter period and this reduces the gross margin if the animals are sold or lowers weight gain at pasture during the subsequent summer.

Veterinary Problems

These are usually few.

1. Transit fever after housing.
2. Infectious bovine rhinotracheitis.
3. Digestive upsets with too rapid introduction of diets to which the animals are unaccustomed.
4. Occasional bloat.
5. Ringworm.
6. Pediculosis.
7. Warts.
8. Mortality during the housed period (six months) is usually low (0.4 *per cent*: range 0.2 - 0.6 *per cent*).

SEMI-INTENSIVE

Overwintering of Stores

This system can involve store animals of varying weights and ages. The aim is to use high roughage diets but to ensure the animals grow so that they are fit but not fat for finishing during the next summer grazing. The system allows a high proportion of by-products to be fed and the aim is to give a minimum of cereal or concentrates.

Type of Animals

Both late and early-maturing breeds and crosses can be used. Usually the cattle are steers rather than heifers.

The System (see Table 7.2)

After purchase the animals are housed and fed sparingly to gain 0.4 - 0.6 kg (0.9 - 1.3 lb) daily. The housed period usually lasts five to six months. The rate of gain will depend on the future destination of the animals. If the cattle are to be finished on the same farm then a gain of 0.4 kg (0.9 lb) daily is satisfactory as it allows the animals to be fit but not fat at turnout in the spring. Early-maturing crosses should also be reared to gain daily at 0.4 kg (0.9 lb). In cattle which are to be sold in the spring, the animals must not look too thin and so a daily gain of 0.6 kg (1.3 lb) is advisable. Late-maturing crosses will also need to be fed at this higher level.

Buildings

Usually the cattle are yarded in straw yards with a space allowance per beast of 1.9 - 4.0 m^2 (20 - 43 ft^2) or on slats with an area of 1.4 - 2.3 m^2 (15 - 25 ft^2). The trough space with restricted feeds is 500 mm (20 in) per animal with a water bowl per 15 cattle or a water trough space of 2000 mm^2 (3.2 in^2) per animal.

TABLE 7.2

Overwintering of Stores - Results

	kg	lb
Feeding period (days)	152	
Daily gain	0.4	0.85
Starting weight	292	640
Weight at sale	350	770
Concentrates used	330	725

(Sources various - including Meat and Livestock Commission)

Advantages

1. Animals are kept for a limited period (five to six months) before a return on capital is obtained.
2. Provided cattle are bought at a competitive price and sold at the right time in the spring, an acceptable gross margin is obtained (about 15 *per cent* of gross returns in a good year).
3. It can make use of arable waste and by-products as well as waste from other feeds.
4. Limited labour is required and is of a non-specialist nature.

Disadvantages

1. The animals can be bought dearly and sold cheaply in the spring. This can lead to a negative gross margin. It is therefore essential to buy animals at the right price.
2. The cost of the store is relatively high (usually about 55 *per cent* of the gross returns, but can be over 80 *per cent* when negative gross margins occur).
3. The cost of feed is high (usually about 15 - 25 *per cent* of the gross returns). The concentrate costs amount to about 60 *per cent* of total feed costs.
4. Often too much concentrate is fed in the winter period and thereby gross margin is reduced if the cattle are sold or lower weight gains occur at grass during the subsequent summer.

Veterinary Problems

These are usually few.

1. Transit fever after housing.
2. Infectious bovine rhinotracheitis.
3. Digestive upsets with too rapid introduction of diets to which the animals are unaccustomed.
4. Occasional bloat.
5. Blackleg.
6. Mortality during the housed period (six months) is usually low (0.3 *per cent*; range 0.2 - 0.5 *per cent*).

INTENSIVE / SEMI-INTENSIVE

Winter (Yard) Finishing of Suckled Calves

These calves are mainly from summer or autumn-born suckler herds. The aim is to feed the animals cheaply but well. Most often silage is fed which has been cut early and has a high digestibility value. Up to 2 kg (4 lb) of concentrates are fed daily. Some farms, however, find the system useful for feeding arable by-products with added concentrates. The system is suitable for both late and early-maturing animals and heifers as well as steers. When the cattle are sold it is often best to match them into groups of similar type and weight.

Type of Animals

All are beef sired often onto cross-bred suckler cows. Heifers and steers can be included.

The System (see Table 7.3)

Following purchase the animals are housed and fed to gain at a daily level of 0.8 kg (1.7 lb). The aim is to finish the animals within about five months. The rate of gain is dependent on the quality of the roughage fed as well as the amount of cereal or concentrate provided. The animals usually produce a carcase of 225 - 250 kg (490 - 550 lb) of good quality with a moderate fat cover.

Buildings

The animals are usually yarded and finished in groups. If straw is used the space allowance is about 1.9 - 4.0 m^2 (20 - 45 ft^2) for 230 - 450 kg (505 - 990 lb) animals, with an area of 1.4 - 2.3 m^2 (15 - 25 ft^2) per beast on slatted accommodation. Feed space should be provided at a minimum of 500 mm (20 in) per beast and if self-feed silage is used, 150 mm (6 in) feed face should be offered per animal unless it is illuminated at night, when it can be reduced. A water bowl should be provided for a maximum of 15 beasts, otherwise 2000 mm^2 (3.2 in^2) of water trough space should be allowed.

TABLE 7.3

Winter (Yard) Finishing of Suckled Calves - Results

	kg	lb
Feeding period (days)	150	
Daily gain	0.7	1.6
Starting weight	305	670
Slaughter weight	410	905
Stocking rate beasts	8.0/hectare	3.2/acre
Concentrates used	0.5 tonne	0.5 ton

(Sources various, including Meat and Livestock Commission).

Advantages

1. The animals are kept for only a limited period (five months) before a return on money is obtained.
2. Provided animals are bought at a competitive price and sold at the right time an acceptable gross margin is obtainable (about 20 per cent of gross returns).
3. The system is versatile and can make use of arable waste and by-products.
4. Often the concentrate feeding can be altered so that cattle can finish sooner or later, depending on market conditions.

Disadvantages

1. If cattle are bought at too expensive a price then a negative gross margin can result.
2. It is often found that too much concentrate is fed to animals of the early-maturing breeds and crosses or to heifers.
3. The cost of the calf is relatively high (usually over 50 per cent of the gross returns and occasionally up to 80 per cent when negative gross margins are obtained).
4. The cost of feed is high (17 - 30 per cent of gross returns). The concentrate cost can be 65 - 75 per cent of the total feed costs.
5. In early-maturing breeds and crosses too much protein may be fed in the concentrate, thereby increasing the feed costs unnecessarily.

Veterinary Problems

Usually these are few.

1. Transit fever.
2. Infectious bovine rhinotracheitis.
3. Digestive upsets if an unusual ration is provided too quickly.
4. Occasional bloat.
5. Abscesses in muscles and subcutaneously.
6. Ringworm.
7. Warts.
8. Mortality during the finishing period (five months) is usually low (0.4 per cent; range 0.2 - 0.5 per cent).
9. Often the yarded animals are very dirty and soiled at the time of slaughter.

Alternatives and Improvements to Winter (Yard) Finishing of Suckled Calves

1. Use of bulls

The use of bulls instead of steers allows increased weight gain and a heavier slaughter weight.

TABLE 7.4

Winter Finishing of Bull and Steer Suckled Calves

	Bulls		Steers	
	kg	lb	kg	lb
Daily liveweight gain	0.9	2.0	0.8	1.8
Slaughter weight	458	1005	414	910
Concentrates fed in finishing period	560	1230	530	1165

There is a 35 per cent increase in gross margin per calf.

Buildings

The animals should be yarded in small groups. It is often best to keep the animals penned tightly. If straw yards are used an area per beast of about 4.0 m^2 (43 ft^2) per beast or on slats 2.3 m^2 (25 ft^2) per animal. The use of slats can be beneficial as the animals are less sure-footed and so they are quieter. Additionally, stockmen do not need to enter the pens for bedding down.

2. Maize silage

Maize silage can be used as an alternative for finishing suckler calves during the winter period.

The System (see Table 7.5)

Suckled steers (often Hereford crosses) are purchased in the autumn and given a diet of maize silage. The liveweight gain should be about 0.9 kg (2 lb) per day, buying at a weight of about 270 kg (595 lb) and being slaughtered at about 430 kg (950 lb). Finishing takes about five to six months. The stocking density is approximately seven beasts per hectare (2.8 beasts per acre) of maize. The daily intake of maize silage is 22 kg (48 lb) plus 0.7 kg (1.5 lb) cereals, 1.4 kg (3 lb) protein concentrate plus some other feeds.

TABLE 7.5

Maize Silage Finishing of Suckled Calves

	kg	lb
Weight at purchase	270	595
Slaughter weight	430	950
Daily weight gain	0.9	2
Maize silage consumed (dry matter)	1.3 tonnes	1.3 tons
Stocking rate (beasts/area)	6.6/hectare	2.6/acre

(Meat and Livestock Commission, 1977)

3. Anabolic Steroids

Ensure minimum implant to slaughter period is observed.

4. Growth Promoters

SEMI-INTENSIVE

Winter (Yard) Finishing of Medium-Weight Stores

Stores are bought in the autumn. The cattle have usually been bought in the spring as light-weight stores, stored at grass in the summer to be sold in the autumn as medium-weight stores. The cattle are derived from beef sires but often they are dairy-bred in origin. In consequence a large number of different breed types may be involved. Heifers can be used in the system and require less concentrate feed. The aim is to feed the animals cheaply but well. Usually silage is fed which should be early-cut with a high digestibility value, and up to 2 kg (4 lb) of concentrates are fed daily. Some farmers use the system for feeding arable by-products with added concentrates. When animals are sold it is often best to match the cattle into groups of similar type and weight.

Type of Animals

Either steers or heifers of early-maturing types are suitable, although some late-maturing beef breeds crossed onto dairy cows may be included.

The System (see Table 7.6)

Following purchase the animals are housed and fed to gain at a daily level of 0.8 kg (1.8 lb). The aim is to slaughter the animals within a period of five months. The rate of gain depends on the quality of the roughage fed as well as the quantity of cereal or concentrate given. The animals usually produce a carcase of 220 - 260 kg (440 - 570 lb), of good quality with a moderate fat cover.

Buildings

The animals are usually housed in groups in yards. If straw is used the space allowance is about 1.9 - 4.0 m^2 (20 - 45 ft^2) for 230 - 450 kg (505 - 990 lb) with an area of 1.4 - 2.3 m^2 (15 - 25 ft^2) per beast on slatted floors. Feeding space should be a minimum of 500 mm (20 in) per animal and if self-fed silage is used, 150 mm (6 in) feed face should be offered per beast unless it is illuminated at night, when the level can be reduced. One water bowl should be provided for a maximum of 15 beasts and if water troughs are used 2000 mm^2 (3.2 in^2) of water trough should be allowed.

TABLE 7.6

Winter (Yard) Finishing of Medium-Weight Stores - Results

	kg	lb
Feeding period (days)	152	
Daily gain	0.8	1.8
Starting weight	315	695
Slaughter weight	430	950
Stocking rate	7.5/hectare	3/acre
Concentrates used	0.5 tonne	0.5 ton

(Sources various - including Meat and Livestock Commission)

Advantages

1. The animals only remain for a limited period (five months) before a return on capital is obtained.

2. Provided cattle are bought at a competitive price and sold at the right time an acceptable gross margin is obtainable (up to about 25 per cent of gross returns).

3. The system is versatile and allows use of arable waste and by-products.

4. The amount of concentrate fed can be altered so that animals can be finished earlier or later, depending on anticipated market trends.

Disadvantages

1. If cattle are purchased at too high a price then a negative gross margin may occur.

2. It is often found that too much concentrate is fed to early-maturing breeds or crosses, or to heifers.

3. The cost of the store is relatively high (up to 70 per cent of the gross returns, but it can be as low as 50 per cent).

4. The cost of feed is high (15 - 25 per cent of gross returns). The concentrate costs are up to 60 - 70 per cent of total feed costs.

5. In early-maturing breeds and crosses too much protein may be fed in the concentrate, thereby increasing the feed costs.

Veterinary Problems

Usually these are few.

1. Transit fever.
2. Infectious bovine rhinotracheitis.
3. Digestive upsets if a change of ration is made too quickly.
4. Occasional bloat.
5. Abscesses in muscles or subcutaneously.
6. Ringworm.
7. Warts.
8. Mortality during the finishing period (five months) is usually low (0.5 per cent; range 0.2 - 0.9 per cent).
9. Often the animals are very dirty or soiled at the time of slaughter.

Alternatives and Improvements to Winter (Yard) Finishing of Medium-Weight Steers

1. Use of Maize Silage

Maize silage is an alternative to the use of more usual silage and concentrate diets and produces similar results. The daily intake of maize silage is 26 kg (57 lb) plus 0.7 kg (1.5 lb) cereals, 1.5 kg (3.3 lb) protein concentrates and 3.5 kg (7.7 lb) other feeds, mainly hay.

TABLE 7.7

Finishing Medium-Weight Stores (Maize Silage)

	kg	lb
Daily liveweight gain	0.8	1.8
Slaughter weight	428	940
Carcase weight	237	520
Maize silage consumed (dry matter)	1.6 tonnes	1.6 tons

SEMI-INTENSIVE

Light-Weight Beef Stores - Stored at Grass

The system is designed to be of very low cost and to make maximum use of grass. If the cattle are not to be kept then often the whole grazing area can be utilised for the animals, thus avoiding the necessity for equipment to conserve hay or silage. However, if sufficient grazing is available for the whole summer period, the appetite of the animals will not be great enough to consume total grass production in the first half of the grazing season.

Type of Animals

These are often spring-born suckler calves of the previous year or dairy-bred animals of about a year which have been yarded during the winter and are sold in the spring as light-weight beef stores. Most are of beef sires but often include the late-maturing breeds. The cattle are usually steers, but may be heifers.

The System (see Table 7.8)

The cattle are bought in the spring and sold in the autumn as medium-weight stores. Management of the grazing is undertaken to ensure maximum utilisation and profitability. Most costs are in the form of fertiliser and seeds. Some hay may be required if the cattle are bought early or the amount of grass available is insufficient prior to sale. Small amounts of concentrates may be fed initially or at the end of the grazing season. The aim is a daily liveweight gain of about 0.8 kg (1.8 lb).

Buildings

None are required except perhaps to isolate ill or injured animals.

TABLE 7.8

Light-Weight Beef Stores - Stored at Grass - Results

	kg		lb
Grazing period (days)		175	
Daily gain	0.7		1.5
Starting weight	210		460
Weight at sale	330		725
Stocking rate	5.3		2.1
Concentrates used	35		76

(Sources various, including Meat and Livestock Commission).

Advantages

1. Animals are kept for a limited period (six months) before a return on capital is obtained.

2. Provided the cattle are bought at a competitive price in the spring and sold at the right time in the autumn, an acceptable gross margin is obtained (about 25 per cent of gross returns).

3. The labour input to the system is very low and no skilled stockmanship is required.

4. No buildings are required.

5. No grass conservation is necessary, although some grass will be wasted in the early spring period if it is not conserved or used for other species or groups of cattle.

6. High stocking rates can ensure high gross margin per hectare/acre.

Disadvantages

1. If cattle are purchased at too high a price in the spring, only a small or negative gross margin may result.

2. The cost of the store is often high. It is often 65 per cent of gross returns although it may go as high as 82 per cent.

3. The main variable cost is fertiliser (2 - 4 per cent of gross returns).

4. Stocking rates may not be sufficiently high. In such cases gross margin per hectare or acre may be low.

5. When gross output of light-weight beef stores in the autumn is low, it is best to overwinter the animals rather than sell them.

6. At the end of the grazing season weight gains can be low.

Veterinary Problems

1. Parasitic gastroenteritis.
2. Parasitic bronchitis (husk).
3. Occasionally liver fluke infestation.
4. Deficiencies such as copper, cobalt, selenium.
5. Hypomagnesaemia.
6. Ringworm.
7. Warts
8. Mortality is variable but on average 1.5 per cent (range 0.8 - 2.5 per cent).

Alternatives and Improvements to Light-Weight Beef Stores - Stored at Grass

1. The use of various grazing systems can improve growth.
2. Anabolic steroids, usually of long action, are best.
3. Growth promoters.

SEMI-INTENSIVE

Finishing Medium-Weight Beef Stores at Grass

The animals involved are of varying ages. The system again is of very low cost and makes maximum use of grass. The number of animals can be adjusted during the season to take into account the amount of grass production.

Type of Animals

These are often late-maturing animals, or early-maturing ones which have been deliberately kept on a low plane of nutrition. Most animals are steers.

The System (See Table 7.9)

Medium-weight stores are bought in the spring. They are put out to grass and allowed to graze with the aim to finish them at the end of the grazing season in the autumn. Success depends on good grassland management. Most costs are in the form of fertilisers and seeds. Some cereal or concentrate may be required at the start of the grazing season or at its end. The aim is a daily liveweight gain of 0.8 kg (1.8 lb) and to slaughter the animals at about 465 kg (1020 lb).

Buildings

As animals are finished off grass, no buildings are necessary, except to house ill or injured animals.

TABLE 7.9

Finishing Medium-Weight Beef Stores on Grass - Results

	kg	lb
Grazing period (days)	176	
Daily gain	0.6	1.4
Starting weight	290	635
Weight at sale	400	880
Stocking rate	5.0/hectare	2.0/acre
Concentrates used	34	75

(Sources various, including Meat and Livestock Commission).

Advantages

1. The animals only remain a limited period (5 to 6 months) before there is a return on capital.

2. Provided the cattle are purchased at a competitive price in the spring and sold at the right price in the autumn, an acceptable gross margin can be gained (usually about 20 per cent of gross returns).

3. The labour requirement is low and not of a specialist nature.

4. No buildings are required.

5. No grass conservation is necessary although some grass may be wasted in the early grazing period if it is not conserved or used for other animals.

6. High stocking rates can ensure high gross margins per hectare/acre.

Disadvantages

1. If cattle are dear at purchase in the spring only a small or even negative gross margin may occur.

2. The cost of the store may be high (70 - 80 per cent of gross returns).

3. The main variable cost is fertiliser (2 - 4 per cent of gross returns).

4. Stocking rates may not be sufficiently high. If this occurs gross margins per hectare or acre are low.

5. Poor weight gains can occur at the end of the grazing season.

Veterinary Problems

1. Parasitic gastroenteritis.
2. Parasitic bronchitis (husk).
3. Occasional liver fluke infestation.
4. Deficiencies such as copper, cobalt or selenium.
5. Hypomagnesaemia.
6. Ringworm.
7. Warts.
8. Mortality is variable at 0.3 per cent (range 0.2 - 0.4 per cent).
9. Often yarded cattle are very dirty or soiled at slaughter.

Alternatives and Improvements to Finishing Medium-Weight Stores Grass

1. The use of various grazing systems can improve gross margin per hectare/acre.

2. Anabolic steroids, usually those of long action, are best.

3. Growth promoters.

SEMI-INTENSIVE / EXTENSIVE

Winter (Yard) Finishing of Heavy Stores

The stores are bought in the autumn, usually off grass. They probably began the year as medium-weight beef stores which were stored at grass in the summer and sold off in the autumn as heavy stores. The cattle are usually derived from a beef sire but they may well be dairy-bred in origin. They may have been through one or two winter store periods previously and in consequence they may be up to three years old. Some of the cattle may have derived from Ireland, shipped over as stores. Almost all the cattle will be steers. The animals are fed a variety of feeds but usually roughage is in the form of good quality silage with a high digestibility value or arable waste or by-products. The stores may receive up to $2^3/_4$ kg (6 lb) concentrate daily. They are often fed to reach a liveweight of up to 520 kg (1150 lb) with a carcase weight of 290 - 300 kg (640 - 660 lb) with a very good quality carcase and medium level of fat cover. When selling the animals it is always best to match them for type and weight.

Type of Animals

Usually steers of Friesian, Charolais cross Friesian, South Devon cross Friesian type, but other types may be used.

The System (see Table 7.10)

Following purchase in the autumn, the cattle are housed and fed to gain at the rate of 0.8 kg (1.8 lb) daily. The aim is to reach slaughter finish in a five-month period. The rate of gain depends on roughage quality and the amount of concentrate fed. The animals usually produce a carcase of 290 - 300 kg (640 - 660 lb) with a good fat cover.

Buildings

The animals are housed in groups, ideally no larger than 20. The yards may contain straw and have a space allowance of 4.0 - 4.6 m^2 (43 - 50 ft^2) per beast of 450 - 540 kg (990 - 1190 lb) or if slats are used the space required is 1.9 - 2.6 m^2 (20 - 28 ft^2). The feeding space should be a minimum of 600 mm (24 in) per beast and if self-fed silage is used 150 mm (6 in) feed face should be offered per animal unless it is illuminated at night, when this level can be reduced. There should be one water bowl per 10 - 12 cattle or, if water troughs are used, the minimum area is 2000 mm^2 (3.2 in^2) per store.

TABLE 7.10

Winter (Yard) Finishing of Heavy Stores

	kg	lb
Feeding period (days)	144	
Daily gain	0.7	1.5
Starting weight	440	970
Slaughter weight	545	1120
Stocking rate	5.5/hectare	1.8/acre
Concentrates used	0.48 tonnes	0.48 tons

(Sources various - including Meat and Livestock Commission)

Advantages

1. The animals remain for a limited period (five months) before a return on capital is obtained.

2. Provided the cattle are bought at a competitive price and sold at the right time, an acceptable gross margin is obtained (up to about 20 per cent of gross returns).

3. The system allows the use of arable waste products or other forms of roughage.

4. The amount of concentrate used can be adjusted to meet earlier or later finishing, depending on market trends.

Disadvantages

1. If cattle are purchased at too high a price, a negative gross margin may result.

2. Often too much concentrate is used in the finishing period and so margins are reduced

3. The cost of the store is high (usually about 65 per cent of the gross returns but it can be as low as 55 per cent or as high as 85 per cent.

4. The cost of feed is relatively high (12 - 20 per cent of gross returns). The concentrate cost is between 50 and 75 per cent of total feed costs.

5. Too much protein is often fed in the concentrate of these late-maturing animals.

Veterinary Problems

These are usually few.

1. Transit fever.
2. Infectious bovine rhinotracheitis.
3. Digestive upsets if diets are altered too quickly.
4. Occasional bloat.
5. Abscesses in muscles or subcutaneously.
6. Ringworm.
7. Warts.
8. Mortality during the finishing period (five months) is usually low at 0.3 per cent (range 0.2 - 0.4 per cent).
9. Often the animals in yards are very dirty or soiled at slaughter.

Alternatives and Improvements to Winter (Yard) Finishing of Heavy Stores

1. Maize silage.
2. Anabolic steroids but ensure minimum implant to slaughter period observed.
3. Growth promoters.

SEMI-INTENSIVE / EXTENSIVE

Medium-Weight Beef Stores - Stored at Grass

The animals are of varying age but all will have had at least one season at grass.

Type of Animals

These are often late-maturing cattle of varying breeds. Many of the cattle have been on a poor level of nutrition. The majority are steers.

The System (see Table 7.11)

The medium-weight stores are bought in the spring. They remain at grass and are allowed to graze for as long as possible - usually an average of six months. Success depends on making maximum use of grass. In some cases numbers are modified according to grass production by buying and selling cattle. Most costs are confined to fertilisers and seeds. Some cereal may be given at the start of the grazing season and towards the time of sale. The animals should ideally gain at a rate of 0.7 kg (1.6 lb) per day.

Buildings

No buildings are required except for housing ill or injured animals.

TABLE 7.11

Medium-Weight Beef Stores - Stored at Grass - Results

	kg	lb
Grazing period (days)	178	
Daily gain	0.6	1.4
Starting weight	290	635
Weight at sale	400	880
Stocking rate	5.0/hectare	2.0/acre
Concentrates used	27	60

(Sources various, including Meat and Livestock Commission).

Advantages

1. The animals only remain for a limited period (about six months) before there is a return on capital.

2. An acceptable gross margin is possible provided the animals are bought at a competitive price in the spring and sold correctly in the autumn. The gross margin is up to 20 per cent of gross returns.

3. The labour requirement is low and is of a non-specialised nature.

4. No buildings are required.

5. No grass conservation is necessary if the cattle are sold in the autumn.

6. A high stocking rate can ensure a good gross margin per hectare/acre.

Disadvantages

1. If the cattle are bought dearly and sold badly only a small or negative gross margin may be achieved.

2. The cost of the store can be relatively high (usually about 75 per cent of gross returns but it can be up to 95 per cent when margins are negative).

3. The main variable cost is fertiliser (2 - 4 per cent of gross returns).

4. If stocking rates are not maximised gross margin per hectare or acre is kept low.

5. Poor weight gains may occur at the end of the grazing season.

Veterinary Problems

1. Parasitic gastroenteritis.
2. Parasitic bronchitis (husk).
3. Occasionally bloat.
4. Deficiencies can occur, including copper, cobalt and selenium.
5. Hypomagnesaemia.
6. Warts.
7. Mortality is low, about 0.3 per cent (range 0.2 - 0.4 per cent).

Alternatives and Improvements to Medium-Weight Beef Stores - Stored at Grass

1. The use of grazing systems increases growth rate.

2. Anabolic steroids may be of use, usually those of long-acting type are best.

3. Growth promoters.

SEMI-INTENSIVE / EXTENSIVE

Finishing Heavy Stores at Grass

The animals can be adjusted according to the amount of grass. It is sometimes possible to have two batches during the grazing season.

Type of Animals

These are often late-maturing animals. Otherwise the cattle are stores from Ireland or they have been kept on a poor plane of nutrition.

The System (see Table 7.12)

Heavy stores (over 390 kg, 860 lb) are purchased in the spring. They are put to grass and are finished off grass as quickly as possible. Some animals will require small quantities of concentrates to finish them.

The cattle are slaughtered at 430 - 570 kg (945 - 1255 lb) with a carcase weight of 205 - 320 kg (450 - 705 lb) of good quality and medium fat cover. If the cattle finish quickly they can be replaced by a second batch.

Buildings

As animals are finished off grass, no buildings are necessary except to house injured or ill animals.

TABLE 7.12

Finishing Heavy Stores at Grass - Results

	kg	lb
Grazing period (days)	140	
Daily gain	0.6	1.4
Starting weight	445	980
Weight at sale	555	1220
Stocking rate	3.5/hectare	1.4/acre
Concentrates used	35	76

Advantages

1. The animals remain on the farm for only a limited time (usually 4 to 5 months) before there is any return on capital.

2. Provided the cattle are bought competitively and sold well then an acceptable gross margin is obtained (about 15 per cent of gross returns).

3. Labour input is minimal and of a non-specialist nature.

4. No buildings are necessary.

5. No grass conservation is required although animals need to be managed properly to ensure the full use of early grass growth.

6. A good gross margin per hectare/acre is obtainable with high stocking rates.

Disadvantages

1. The system can produce very low or negative gross margins if animals are badly bought or sold.

2. The cost of the store is often high (80 to 85 per cent of gross returns).

3. The main variable cost is fertiliser (2 to 4 per cent of gross returns).

4. Stocking rates may not be sufficiently high. In these circumstances gross margin per hectare/acre may be low.

5. Usually the price per unit weight (i.e. kg or lb) is lower than for lighter animals.

6. At the end of the grazing season some of the cattle may not be finished and may require yarding.

Veterinary Problems

Usually these are few.

1. Parasitic gastroenteritis, but usually animals are relatively immune.
2. Parasitic bronchitis (husk).
3. Occasionally liver fluke.
4. Mineral deficiencies, e.g. cobalt, copper, selenium.
5. Hypomagnesaemia.
6. Warts.
7. Low mortality rate, usually about 0.2 per cent (range 0.1 - 0.4 per cent).

Alternatives and Improvements to Finishing Heavy Stores on Grass

1. Skilled use of grazing system.

2. Anabolic steroids, but these should be of the long-acting type.

3. Growth promoters.

Reference

MEAT AND LIVESTOCK COMMISSION (1977) Data Sheets. Meat and Livestock Commission, Bletchley. pp. 1-72.

CHAPTER 8

REARING BREEDING REPLACEMENTS

REARING REPLACEMENTS FOR DAIRY AND SUCKLER HERDS

Two-Year Calving

Although there is a trend towards two-year calving, it is still not commonly performed successfully. Many suckler herds do not rear their own replacements but buy in in-calf or bulling heifers. The origin of the calves is usually dairy herds, and these may then be reared. Dairy herd replacements are usually reared on their home farm. However, some farmers specialise in heifer rearing and a few farmers have their replacements reared elsewhere. As the tendency is for cows to have a calving index or interval greater than 12 months, in herds with a tight calving pattern the aim is to calve the heifers at about 22 or 23 months rather than 24 months.

Type of Animals

The majority of suckler replacements are Hereford cross Friesians from the dairy herd. These tend to produce sufficient milk and are usually of good temperament, allowing fostering to be undertaken. Dairy cattle will be mainly Friesian cross Holstein, although many breeds are reared in small numbers for dairy and beef purposes.

The System

The aim is often to try to have the heifers calving at about two years old.

Autumn-Born Heifer Calf Rearing

The system is often based on calves born from November to March which are early-weaned. During the housed period they should be given roughage (probably hay) and concentrates to produce a daily gain of 0.6 kg (1.3 lb) so that at turnout the weight for Friesian heifers is 150 kg (330 lb) or about 30 per cent of mature body weight.

First Grazing Season

They are turned out to grass in the spring as soon as possible. Good growth is ensured by the provision of supplementary barley feed during the first two weeks of the grazing season, if the calves will accept it. The aim is to obtain a daily liveweight gain of 0.65 kg (1.4 lb) and a weight at the end of the grazing season of 265 kg (580 lb). Towards the end of the grazing season some supplementary feeding, at the rate of about 1.5 kg (3 lb) per day, will be required to maintain weight gain.

Second Winter Housing

During the autumn the cattle are yarded and receive hay or silage and about 1.5 kg (3 lb) concentrates per day. The cattle are put into calf, usually by natural service, when around 15 months old. The animals at this stage grow at about 0.7 kg (1.5 lb) per day prior to mating, and then 0.5 kg (1.2 lb) after mating. The minimum weight at mating for Hereford cross Friesian heifers should be 325 kg (715 lb), for Aberdeen Angus cross Friesian 290 kg (640 lb), for Friesian 330 kg (720 lb), Ayrshire 420 kg (925 lb), Jersey 335 kg (505 lb) and Guernsey 260 kg (575 lb). The animals are housed at about 375 kg (825 lb). They are ideally thin but fit, at a condition score of about 2½.

Second Grazing Season

Following turnout in the spring, the animals make use of compensatory gain to produce a daily gain of 0.7 kg (1.5 lb) to calving, with the Friesian heifer weighing 510 kg (1125 lb). Good grassland management means that no supplementary feeding is necessary until late summer. The condition score at calving should be 3 to 3½. Hereford cross Friesian heifers calve at a weight of 475 kg (1045 lb), Aberdeen Angus cross Friesian at 430 kg (950 lb), Ayrshire 420 kg (925 lb), Jersey 335 kg (740 lb) and Guernsey 385 kg (850 lb).

Autumn-Born Suckled Calves

These will obviously be with their dams during the first winter housing period and they tend to remain with them in the subsequent grazing period. Because the calf receives milk as well as hay and concentrates in the winter and grass in the summer, the daily liveweight gain tends to be better than that of the dairy calf. By six months of age the calf weighs between 35 and 40 per cent of the mature cow's body weight.

Spring-Born Heifer Calf Rearing

These calves are born in the late winter to early summer and are again early-weaned. They are fed hay and concentrates until turnout.

First Grazing Season

Ideally the animals go out to grass as soon as possible when about 3 to 4 months old. They are usually able to graze up to five months until the autumn, and should achieve a daily liveweight gain of 0.55 kg (1.3 lb) so that at housing they weigh 140 kg (310 lb).

Second Winter Housing

The animals are yarded and then usually receive silage or hay and a small amount of concentrates (e.g. rolled barley). Gain is at a level of 0.6 kg (1.4 lb) daily so that at turnout the cattle weigh 255 kg (560 lb).

Second Grazing Season

The animals return to grass early in the spring. They will usually grow well during this period, gaining about 0.7 kg (1.5 lb) daily. The heifers are introduced to the bull or inseminated when about 15 months old and at a weight of 325 kg (715 lb). At housing the cattle weigh about 370 kg (820 lb).

Third Winter Housing

The cattle are yarded and during the winter receive silage and concentrates. They gain at about 0.6 kg (1.4 lb) daily. They either calve indoors or soon after going to pasture. The weight at calving should be 475 kg (1045 lb).

Spring-Born Suckled Calves

These will again be on their dams at pasture until weaning at about seven months old. At this time Blue Grey and Aberdeen Angus cross calves will weigh 180 kg (400 lb) having gained weight at the rate of 0.7 kg

(1.5 lb) daily. During the winter period only a low daily gain is required - 0.3 kg (0.7 lb) so that at turnout, when just over a year old, they weigh 240 kg (530 lb). Once outside, the heifers should gain at 0.7 kg (1.5 lb) daily, reaching a weight of 280 kg (615 lb) by 15 months old when the animals are served. They should then gain at about 0.6 kg (1.3 lb) daily until yarding at a weight of 355 kg (780 lb). During the five months or so up to calving, weight should increase at 0.5 kg (1.1 lb) daily so that the cattle weigh 430 kg (950 lb) at 24 months old. The same weights can be used as a guide for Luing and Welsh Black pure-bred heifers. However for Hereford cross, Lincoln Red cross and Devon crosses, all the weights need to be increased. In the case of Highland and Galloway pure-bred cattle, the weights need decreasing.

Buildings

Specialist accommodation will be required by the calves if bought in plus some form of follow-on accommodation. Suckler calves run with their dams if autumn-born. For spring-born calves, during the first winter, straw yards with an area of 1.5 - 3.0 m^2 (15 - 32 ft^2) are suitable, but a larger area is required for autumn-born heifers of 3.0 - 4.0 m^2 (32 - 42 ft^2). Although slatted floors can be used for heifers, it is probably best not to use them, particularly as the animals become heavier in weight.

Advantages

1. A reduction in the amount of forage required and therefore in the land requirement.

2. The gross margin is not as high as with later calving but it is received in two years (about 42 *per cent* of gross returns in spring-born compared with 49 *per cent* in two-and-a-half year animals. The levels for autumn-born calves are 38 *per cent* for two-year calving and 41 *per cent* for two-and-a-half year calving.

3. The gross margin per unit area tends to be improved (about 15 *per cent* better) when compared with later calving, indicating a reduced demand on land.

4. Housing requirements tend to be lower than with later calving.

Disadvantages

1. More concentrates are needed (915 kg (18 cwt) spring-born; 710 kg (14 cwt) autumn-born) than for rearing at lower levels. Two-and-a-half year calving required, 570 kg (11.2 cwt) spring-born and 610 kg (12 cwt) autumn-born. Therefore concentrate costs tend to be high - about 24 *per cent* of gross output in spring-born calves and 19 *per cent* for autumn-born.

2. It is often difficult to reach a two-year calving level unless service starts earlier than 15 months.

3. The animals must be well-grown at the time of insemination and calving to prevent dystokia problems.

4. In some studies with dairy cows, animals have become overfat and have not milked well in their first lactation.

5. Forage costs are lower (13 *per cent* of gross returns) than for two-and-a-half year calving (17 *per cent*).

6. Two-year calving means there are less non-calved replacements required. Thus with a 20 per cent replacement ratio only 40 are kept per 100 cows.

7. Land requirements are minimal (see page 146).

Veterinary Problems

Calf Period

1. Adequate colostrum.
2. Coli-septicaemia/coli-enteritis.
3. Viral diarrhoea.
4. Salmonellosis.
5. Enzootic pneumonia.
6. Ringworm.
7. Pediculosis.

Rearing Period

1. Infectious bovine keratoconjunctivitis (New Forest eye).
2. Parasitic gastroenteritis.
3. Parasitic bronchitis (husk).
4. Liver fluke infestation.
5. Mineral deficiencies such as copper, cobalt, selenium.
6. Pasteurellosis on housing.
7. Hypomagnesaemia.

Pregnancy

1. Abortion, such as salmonellosis, *S. dublin*, leptospirosis, brucellosis, mycotic abortion.

2. Dystokia - levels of dystokia in heifers twice that in cows.

REARING REPLACEMENTS FOR DAIRY AND SUCKLER HERDS

Two-and-a-Half-Year Calving

Many heifers in both dairy and suckler herds to calve at around 2½ years of age. However, several of such animals are failures from attempted two-year calving. Most suckler herds buy in their replacements, often at bulling or in-calf. Previously these animals have often been reared by specialist rearers. Most dairy replacements are brought up on their farms from birth. However, some farms do buy in heifers from rearers or they contract out the rearing of their replacements to reduce requirements on valuable land. The 2½-year system is much easier to achieve than the two-year calving plan. The aim is also to produce a heifer which is heavier at both mating and calving than is possible under the two-year calving system. At 2½-year calving it means that the heifers in herds with a tight calving patterns will calve six months out of sequence.

Type of Animals

Most suckler herd cows are Hereford cross Friesians although other breeds may be involved, including the Blue-Grey (White Shorthorn cross Galloway). Dairy cattle tend to be pure-bred Friesian, Holstein or Holstein cross Friesian although many other breeds, both beef and dairy, are reared in small numbers.

The System

The aim is to have the heifers calving at about 2½ years old.

Autumn-Born Calf Rearing

The calf is early-weaned at about five weeks old. She is then fed usually on hay but possibly silage plus some concentrates until turnout at six months old. Daily liveweight gain for Friesian heifers should be about 0.5 kg (1.1 lb) with a weight at turnout of about 130 kg (290 lb).

First Grazing Season

Turnout occurs early in spring and the cattle then gain at the rate of 0.5 kg (1.1 lb) until yarding in the autumn. Usually no concentrates are necessary during this period. Grazing usually lasts about six months and the weight of the heifers at yarding is about 230 (500 lb).

Second Winter Housing

During the winter period the cattle are fed hay or silage and a small quantity of concentrates to gain at about 0.5 kg (1.0 lb) daily. Thus at the end of the yarding period, which lasts about six months, the cattle weigh about 310 kg (680 lb).

Second Grazing Season

The cattle are 18 months old at this stage and lean, and will produce good compensatory gains at grass during the first half of the grazing season. Thus by the time of service at 21 months of age, the condition score should be about 3 to 3½. The overall daily gain during the grazing period is about 0.6 kg (1.3 lb) so that the animals are yarded at 420 kg (925 lb). Again no concentrates should need to be fed in the grazing period.

Third Winter Housing

The cattle will receive hay and silage plus some concentrates during the yarding period with the aim of gaining 0.5 kg (1.2 lb) daily so that by calving the heifers weigh at least 510 kg (1120 lb).

Autumn-Born Suckled Calves

The calf is with the dam and so will receive milk as well as hay and concentrates. Following turnout the calf will graze, and this will be supplemented with milk. Thus the weight gains up to the second winter housing will tend to be higher than for dairy heifers. Subsequently the system is similar although the daily weight gain in the second housing period can be reduced to 0.4 kg (0.9 lb) daily for a Hereford cross Friesian calf or 0.3 kg for a Blue-Grey or Aberdeen Angus cross calf.

Spring-Born Calf Rearing

The calf is again early-weaned at about five weeks old. They then receive hay or possibly silage with concentrates up to turnout at about three to four months old. Only a low daily gain of 0.5 kg (1 lb) is required so the animals are turned out at about 80 kg (175 lb).

First Grazing Season

The calves should live exclusively off grass to gain at a rate of 0.5 kg (1.0 lb) daily so that by the time of yarding the animals weigh 125 kg (280 lb).

Second Winter Housing

During the winter period the cattle continue to grow at a low daily liveweight gain of 0.5 kg (1.0 lb). They receive hay or silage and a small amount of concentrates. At the end of the second housing period when the cattle are about a year old their weight is 200 kg (440 lb).

Second Grazing Season

The animals go out to grass early in a thin condition and make maximum utilisation of compensatory growth. The daily gain of 0.6 kg (1.3 lb) can be aimed at so that by the end of the period the cattle weigh about 340 kg (750 lb).

Third Winter Housing

The cattle receive hay or silage and some concentrates during the winter period with the aim of gaining 0.5 kg (1.1 lb) daily. The heifers are served during the housed period and at turnout they weigh about 420 kg (925 lb).

Third Grazing Period

During the final summer the heifers graze all season with little or no supplementary feeding. They gain at a daily rate of 0.7 kg (1.5 lb) so that they calve at a weight of 510 kg (1120 lb).

Spring-Born Suckled Calves

The calf will be heavier when weaning at seven months old than the dairy heifer as it has been able to supplement its grazing with milk. During the second (or first) winter housing, depending on time of birth and management, daily liveweight gain can be kept to about 0.4 kg (0.9 lb) daily for a Hereford cross Friesian or 0.3 kg (0.7 lb) daily for a Blue-Grey or Aberdeen Angus cross calf.

Buildings

Specialist calf accommodation is required for calves bought in and then some follow-on buildings. Suckler calves will be with their dams if autumn-born. During the second winter, straw yard accommodation for spring-born cattle can be 1.5 - 3.0 m^2 (15 - 32 ft^2), but greater space is required for autumn-born cattle - 3.0 - 4.0 m^2 (32 - 42 ft^2). In the third winter the spring and autumn-born calves will require 4.0 - 4.6 m^2 (42 - 49 ft^2). Although slatted floors can be used, they are probably not ideal for use with heifers, particularly when they become heavier in weight.

Advantages

1. The system is simple and the targets are much easier to obtain than those of two-year calving.

2. The amount of concentrate used should be less than for two-year rearing. For spring-born animals the level is 570 kg (11.2 cwt) as opposed to 915 kg (18 cwt) for two-year calving. Autumn-born animals have levels of 610 kg (12 cwt) and 710 kg (14 cwt) respectively. Thus concentrate costs are lower at about 14 per cent of gross returns in autumn-born calves and 16 per cent in spring-born animals.

3. Gross margin is higher (49 per cent of gross returns) compared with 42 per cent for two-year calving with spring-born calves. The respective levels for autumn-born calves are 41 per cent of gross returns for 2½-year calving and 38 per cent for two year calving.

4. More use is made of forage in the system and in consequence forage costs are higher. In autumn-born calves the level is about 17 per cent of gross returns compared with 13 per cent for two-year calving. Likewise, with spring-born calves, the respective levels are 17 and 13 per cent.

5. The animals are better grown than for two-year calving and so dystokia is less likely to be a problem.

6. With 2½-year calving less non-calved replacements are kept on the farm i.e. if replacement rate is 20 per cent then only 50 are kept per 100 cows.

Disadvantages

1. The system takes two-and-a-half years so there is a long period before a return on capital.

2. The demand for land is greater than with two-year calving. Thus the gross margin per unit area (i.e. hectare/acre) is about 15 per cent less than that for earlier calving.

3. Forage costs are higher than for two-year calving.

4. There is an extra period of housing and so the accommodation requirements are considerably higher than for two-year calving.

5. In a herd with a tight calving pattern the heifers will be calving six months out of alignment with the main herd.

6. Land requirements are relatively high (see Table 8.1).

Veterinary Problems

Calf Period

1. Adequate colostrum.
2. Coli-septicaemia/coli-enteritis.
3. Viral diarrhoea.
4. Salmonellosis.
5. Enzootic pneumonia.
6. Ringworm.
7. Pediculosis.

Rearing Period

1. Infectious bovine keratoconjunctivitis (New Forest eye).
2. Parasitic gastroenteritis.
3. Parasitic bronchitis (husk).
4. Possible liver fluke.
5. Mineral deficiencies such as cobalt, copper, selenium.
6. Pasteurellosis on housing.
7. Hypomagnesaemia.

Pregnancy

1. Abortion such as brucellosis, leptospirosis, mycotic, salmonellosis. S. dublin.
2. Dystokia levels in heifers twice that of cows.

REARING REPLACEMENTS FOR DAIRY AND SUCKLER HERDS

Three-Year Calving

This system has been used traditionally. However, it does require much capital investment before there is any return. The system needs little expensive input although there is an increased land requirement for grazing and conserved forage production. There are fewer problems and less pressure in ensuring that heifers become pregnant at the required time. Although frowned on by progressive advisers, it is still a fact that many heifers in both suckler and dairy herds do calve at three years old, whether by accident or design. Most suckler herds buy in their replacements often in-calf or bulling. Previously these cattle have, in many cases, been reared by specialist rearers. Most dairy replacements are brought up on their farms of origin. However, in order to reduce demands on valuable land resources, some farmers buy in replacements or contract out the rearing of their heifers. The three-year system is often deliberately used with late-maturing breeds such as the Highland, Galloway or Welsh Black and it tends also to be undertaken in areas with poor grazing, such as hill and upland conditions. The use of 2½-year calving means that in herds with a tight calving pattern the heifers calve six months out of sequence and so, as this may not be acceptable, three-year calving may be used.

Type of Animals

Although some Friesian, Holstein and Friesian cross Holstein cattle are reared under this system, it is now becoming rarer. It is an unusual system for early-maturing beef breeds and their crosses such as the Hereford and crosses, Aberdeen Angus and crosses, etc., although it can be used for late-maturing animals such as the Galloway, Highland, Welsh Black, etc.

The System

The aim is to have the heifers calving at about three years old.

Autumn-Born Calf Rearing

The calf is still reared in a similar way as for other systems to ensure that it is strong and healthy. Early-weaning occurs at about five weeks old and is followed by feeding with hay or possibly silage and a small amount of concentrates. Turnout is at about six months old and, for Friesian heifers, at a weight of about 110 kg (240 lb), having gained at about 0.45 kg (1 lb) daily.

First Grazing Season

Turnout is usually early in the spring and the calves gain at a rate of about 0.5 kg (1.1 lb) daily until yarding. The aim is not to feed concentrates during this period. Grazing usually continues for about six months and by the autumn the animals weigh about 200 kg (440 lb).

Second Winter Housing

During the winter period the animals are fed to gain at about 0.4 kg (0.9 lb) daily. They receive hay or silage with minimal amounts of concentrates. The yarding period lasts about six months and by its end the animals weigh about 275 kg (605 lb).

Second Grazing Season

The cattle are now about 18 months old and as they are thin they can make the most of compensatory gain. However, often the grazing is poor or stocking is such as to prevent large weight gains. The animals then have a daily gain of about 0.5 kg (1.1 lb). Again the period lasts about six months so that the weight gain at the end of the time is about 370 kg (814 lb).

Third Winter Period

The cattle again receive hay or silage and usually along the line a small amount of concentrates. Weight gain is about 0.5 kg (1.1 lb) up to service and it continues at just less than this following pregnancy. The animals weigh about 460 kg (1015 lb) at turnout.

Third Grazing Period

At grass the cattle continue to grow at about 0.5 - 0.6 kg (1.1 - 1.3 lb) daily so that at calving the weight of the cattle may be as much as 550 kg (1210 lb). Ideally at calving the condition score should be 3 to 3½.

Autumn-Born Suckled Calves

As the calf is with the cow, it receives milk as well as concentrates and hay or silage. Following turnout, the calf will again receive milk supplementation and so the weight gain up to the end of grazing will be greater than for dairy heifers. Thus in the second housing period weight gains may be low, being only 0.3 kg (0.7 lb) daily for Blue-Grey or Galloway cattle. Subsequently the cattle follow a similar management system.

Spring-Born Calf Rearing

The calf is again early-weaned at about five weeks old. They receive hay or possibly silage with concentrates to gain at a rate of 0.5 kg (1.0 lb) daily for Friesian heifers. At turnout the animals are all about three to four months old at about 80 kg (175 lb) liveweight.

First Grazing Season

The calves feed off grass to gain daily at about 0.5 kg (1.1 lb) until they are yarded about three months later at a weight of 125 kg (280 lb).

Second Winter Housing

During the six months housing, calves grow at a daily liveweight gain of 0.4 kg (0.9 lb). They receive restricted amounts of hay or silage and a little concentrate so that at turnout they weigh 180 kg (395 lb).

Second Grazing Period

The animals go to grass early in a thin condition and make use of compensatory gain. This gain is normally at about 0.5 kg (1.0 lb) daily until yarding in the autumn. The level is low because of the poor grazing or type of animal kept. At yarding the animals weigh about 270 kg (595 lb).

Third Winter Housing

The cattle again receive hay or silage with the aim of gaining 0.45 kg (1.0 lb) daily. Usually little or no concentrates are fed. At turnout the animals weigh about 350 kg (770 lb).

Third Grazing Period

The cattle graze all season and in the first half daily weight gain is about 0.6 kg (1.3 lb). The animals are bulled at about mid-grazing season when they are about 27 months old. Subsequent weight gain is about 0.5 kg (1.1 lb). Weight at time of yarding is about 450 kg (990 lb).

Fourth Winter Housing

During the yarding the cattle gain at about 0.5 kg (1.0 lb) daily. Usually only small quantities of concentrates are fed and the main diet is hay or silage. At calving the cattle weigh about 540 kg (1190 lb).

Spring-Born Suckled Calves

The calf will be heavier at weaning than the dairy calf because of the milk provided by the dam in addition to the grazing. During the second (or in this case probably the first) winter housing, weight gain will, at the most, be 0.35 kg (0.8 lb) daily. Subsequently the system is similar to that for the dairy heifer.

Buildings

Specialist calf accommodation is required for those calves which have been bought in, plus follow-on accommodation. Suckler calves will be in yards with their dams if autumn-born. During the second winter housing the spring-born calf requires 1.1 - 1.9 m^2 (12 - 20 ft^2) of straw yard whereas the autumn-born calf probably needs 1.9 - 4.0 m^2 (20 - 42 ft^2). During the third winter housing the spring-born calf requires 3.0 - 4.0 m^2 (32 - 42 ft^2) whereas the autumn-born calf needs just over 4.0 m^2 (42 ft^2). The fourth winter for the spring-born heifers will require straw yards of about 4.6 m^2 (49 ft^2). Although slatted floors can be used, they are probably not best for use with heifers, particularly as they become heavier in weight.

Advantages

1. The system is very simple and any targets can be easily met.

2. There is versatility in the system which will allow weight gains to be increased and thereby decrease the age at service and subsequent calving.

3. The gross margin tends to be higher or equal to that for two-year calving and higher than that of autumn-born heifers calving at 2½ years (42 per cent of the gross returns for spring-born heifers and 39 per cent for autumn-born heifers).

4. The amount of concentrate used should be lower than for either two or 2½-year calving (10 per cent of the gross returns for spring calving and seven per cent for autumn calving).

5. The system has relatively low capital inputs so that the total variable costs tend to be lower or the same as for autumn and spring-born heifers calving at two years (42 per cent of total returns for spring-born heifers and 38 per cent for autumn-born replacements), and lower than those for autumn-born heifers calving at 2½ years.

Disadvantages

1. A larger amount of forage and therefore land is required than for the two or 2½-year calving systems.

2. Forage costs amount to 23 per cent of the gross returns for both spring and autumn-born heifers.

3. There is a large demand for buildings prior to the cattle entering the milking herd.

4. The amount of dystokia tends to be less than that for two-year calving but may be higher than for the 2½-year system.

5. The gross margin per unit area (hectare/acre) tends to be lower than in the other systems.

6. Often the amount of concentrates used in the system is far in excess of that required theoretically.

7. Third-year calving means more non-calved replacements in the herd i.e. for a 20 per cent replacement rate, 60 cattle are required for every 100 cows.

8. Land requirements are high (see Table 8.11).

Veterinary Problems

Calf Period

1. Adequate colostrum.
2. Coli-septicaemia/coli-enteritis.
3. Viral diarrhoea.
4. Salmonellosis.
5. Enzootic pneumonia.
6. Ringworm.
7. Pediculosis.

Rearing Period

1. Infectious bovine keratoconjunctivitis (New Forest eye).
2. Parasitic gastroenteritis.
3. Parasitic bronchitis (husk).
4. Possibly liver fluke.
5. Mineral deficiencies such as cobalt, copper, selenium.
6. Hypomagnesaemia.
7. Pasteurellosis at housing.

Pregnancy

1. Abortion such as brucellosis, leptospirosis, mycotic, salmonellosis, _S. dublin_.

2. Dystokia levels in heifers are twice that in cows.

Contract Rearing of Heifer Replacements

Some dairy farmers have considerable pressure on their land resources and in such cases contract rearing of heifers may provide an answer. It thus effectively gives the farmer access to extra land which need not be adjacent to his own holding. The system allows the farmer to choose his own breeding policy which is not the case when purchasing replacements. The main problem is to ensure that the heifers are reared adequately, particularly if the other farm is some distance from the dairy herd. Additionally, there is a considerable capital outlay required for contract payments and A.I. fees. For contract rearing to be profitable for the owner it must be shown that the facilities vacated will be more profitably used or result in an expansion of the business. Obviously the advantage for the rearer is that he will receive an income without investment in the animals. The main veterinary problem is that there is always a possibility that the return of the heifers will introduce diseases if other cattle are kept at the rearer's farm.

Purchasing Heifer Replacements

Some dairy farmers buy in bulling or in-calf heifers, and most suckler herds buy in their replacements. This again gets over the problem of pressure on land resources and is equivalent to giving the farmer access to extra land. There is no capital investment tied up in replacements but obviously the cost of buying the heifers will vary considerably at different times. However, the farmer will not be able to select the breeding of his animals and there is always the possibility of introducing disease.

Home-Rearing of Replacements

Most dairy farmers undertake rearing of their own heifer replacements. This then allows them to keep control of their rearing and performance. Obviously it does tie up land which might otherwise be more profitably used and it can reduce the possibility of expansion. However, where two-year calving of heifers is practised then the land utilised is minimal. Home-rearing does mean that the farmer is able to control his own breeding programme and it also minimises the risk of introduction of disease, as in most cases either artificial insemination is used, or the only animal which need periodically be bought in is a bull. The main problem with home-rearing is the capital invested in the rearing and A.I. costs. Stockman expertise must be available, particularly during the calf rearing period.

TABLE 8.1

Targets for Weight Gain for Friesian Heifers

Autumn-Born Calves Reared as Heifer Replacements

	2-Year Calving		2½-Year Calving		3-Year Calving	
Daily Liveweight Gain	kg	lb	kg	lb	kg	lb
Calf rearing	0.5	1.2	0.5	1.1	0.5	1.0
Post weaning	0.7	1.4	0.5	1.1	0.5	1.0
First grazing season	0.7	1.4	0.5	1.1	0.5	1.1
Second winter housing (pre-mating)	0.7	1.4	0.5	1.0	0.4	0.9
(post-mating)	0.5	1.2				
Second grazing season	0.7	1.5	0.6	1.3	0.5	1.1
Third winter housing			0.5	1.2	0.5	1.2
Third grazing season					0.5	1.1

	2-Year Calving		2½-Year Calving		3-Year Calving	
Weight at End of Period	kg	lb	kg	lb	kg	lb
Calf rearing	150	330	130	290	110	240
First grazing season	265	580	230	500	200	440
Second winter housing	370	820	310	680	275	605
Second grazing season	510	1125	420	925	370	814
Third winter housing			510	1120	460	1015
Third grazing season					530	1165

TABLE 8.2

Targets for Weight Gain for Friesian Heifers

Spring-Born Calves Reared as Heifer Replacements

Daily Liveweight Gain	2-Year Calving kg	2-Year Calving lb	2½-Year Calving kg	2½-Year Calving lb	3-Year Calving kg	3-Year Calving lb
Calf rearing	0.5	1.2	0.5	1.0	0.5	1.0
First grazing season	0.6	1.3	0.5	1.0	0.5	1.1
Second winter housing	0.6	1.4	0.5	1.0	0.4	0.9
Second grazing season	0.7	1.5	0.6	1.3	0.5	1.0
Third housing period	0.6	1.4	0.5	1.1	0.5	1.0
Third grazing period			0.7	1.5	0.6	1.3
Fourth winter housing					0.5	1.0

Weight at End of Period	2-Year Calving kg	2-Year Calving lb	2½-Year Calving kg	2½-Year Calving lb	3-Year Calving kg	3-Year Calving lb
Calf rearing	80	175	80	175	80	175
First grazing season	140	310	125	280	125	280
Second winter housing	255	560	200	440	180	395
Second grazing period	370	820	340	750	270	595
Third winter housing	475	1045	420	925	350	770
Third grazing period			510	1120	450	990
Fourth winter housing					540	1190

TABLE 8.3

Amount of Feed Consumed by Autumn-Born Friesian Calves
Reared as Heifer Replacements Calving at Two Years

	Milk Substitute		Concentrates		Hay	or	Silage	
	kg	lb	kg	cwt	tonnes	tons	tonnes	tons
Calf rearing	13	28	20	0.5	-	-	-	-
Post weaning	-	-	305	6	0.36	0.35 or		
					0.1	0.1 and	1	1
First grazing season	-	-	102	2	-	-	-	-
Second winter housing	-	-	255	5	1.5	1.5 or	4.5	4.5
Second grazing season	-	-	-	-	-	-	-	-
TOTAL	13	28	682	13.5	1.9	1.9	5.5	5.5
							plus hay	
							0.1	0.1

TABLE 8.4

Amount of Feed Consumed by Spring-Born Friesian Calves
Reared as Heifer Replacements Calving at Two Years

	Milk Substitute		Concentrates		Hay	or	Silage	
	kg	lb	kg	cwt	tonnes	tons	tonnes	tons
Calf rearing	13	28	100	2	0.1	0.1	-	-
First grazing season	-	-	100	2	-	-	-	-
Second winter housing	-	-	305	6	0.75	0.75	2.75	2.75
Second grazing season	-	-	50	1	-	-	-	-
Third winter housing	-	-	355	7	1.25	1.25	4.5	4.5
TOTAL	13	28	910	18	2.1	2.1	7.25	7.25

TABLE 8.5

Amount of Feed Consumed by Autumn-Born Friesian Calves
Reared as Heifer Replacements Calving at 2½ Years

	Milk Substitute		Concentrates		Hay	or	Silage	
	kg	lb	kg	cwt	tonnes	tons	tonnes	tons
Calf rearing	13	28	20	0.5	-	-	-	-
Post weaning	-	-	205	4	0.25 0.1	0.25 or 0.1 and	0.5	0.5
First grazing season	-	-	-	-	-	-	-	-
Second winter housing	-	-	152	3	1	1	3.5	3.5
Second grazing season	-	-	-	-	-	-	-	-
Third winter housing	-	-	205	4	1.5	1.5	5	5
TOTAL	13	28	582	11.5	2.75	2.75	9 plus 0.1	9 hay 0.1

TABLE 8.6

Amount of Feed Consumed by Spring-Born Friesian Calves
Reared as Heifer Replacements Calving at 2½ Years

	Milk Substitute		Concentrates		Hay	or	Silage	
	kg	lb	kg	cwt	tonnes	tons	tonnes	tons
Calf rearing	13	28	100	2	0.1	0.1	-	-
First grazing season	-	-	100	2	-	-	-	-
Second winter housing	-	-	152	3	0.6	0.6	2.25	2.25
Second grazing season	-	-	-	-	-	-	-	-
Third winter housing	-	-	152	3	1.25	1.25	4.5	4.5
Third grazing season	-	-	-	-	-	-	-	-
TOTAL	13	28	504	10	1.95	1.95	6.75	6.75

TABLE 8.7

Amount of Feed Consumed by Autumn-Born Friesian Calves Reared as Heifer Replacements Calving at Three Years

	Milk Substitute		Concentrates		Hay	or	Silage	
	kg	lb	kg	cwt	tonnes	tons	tonnes	tons
Calf rearing	13	28	20	0.5	-	-	-	-
Post weaning	-	-	100	2.0	0.25 0.1	0.25 or 0.1 and	0.4	0.4
First grazing season	-	-	-	-	-	-	-	-
Second winter housing	-	-	50	1.0	1	1	3.5	3.5
Second grazing season	-	-	-	-	-	-	-	-
Third winter housing	-	-	80	1.5	1.25	1.25	4.5	4.5
Third grazing season	-	-	-	-	-	-	-	-
TOTAL	13	28	250	5.0	2.5	2.5	8.4 plus 0.1	8.4 hay 0.1

TABLE 8.8

Amount of Feed Consumed by Spring-Born Friesian Calves Reared as Heifer Replacements Calving at Three Years

	Milk Substitute		Concentrates		Hay	or	Silage	
	kg	lb	kg	cwt	tonnes	tons	tonnes	tons
Calf rearing	13	28	100	2.0	0.1	0.1	-	-
First grazing season	-	-	100	2.0	-	-	-	-
Second winter housing	-	-	80	1.5	0.6	0.6	2.25	2.25
Second grazing season	-	-	-	-	-	-	-	-
Third winter housing	-	-	-	-	1.0	1.0	3.5	3.5
Third grazing season	-	-	-	-	-	-	-	-
Fourth winter housing	-	-	80	1.5	1.25	1.25	4.5	4.5
TOTAL	13	28	360	7.0	2.95	2.95	10.25	10.25

TABLE 8.9

Weights at Service and Pre-Calving for Various Breeds Used for Two-Year Calving

	Weight at Service		Weight Pre-Calving	
	kg	lb	kg	lb
DAIRY				
Ayrshire	280	615	420	925
Friesian	325	720	510	1125
Guernsey	260	575	390	850
Jersey	230	505	335	740
BEEF				
Aberdeen Angus crosses	280	615	425	935
Aberdeen Angus x Friesian	290	640	430	950
Blue Grey	280	615	425	935
Galloway	260	575	400	880
Hereford crosses	300	660	455	1000
Hereford x Friesian	320	705	490	1080
Highland	245	540	365	805
Luing	280	615	420	925
Red breeds and their crosses	335	740	510	1125
Welsh Black	290	640	435	960

(After M.L.C./M.M.B., 1976)

TABLE 8.10

Target Weights for Replacement Suckler Cow Heifers at Two Years of Age

	Daily Gain			
	Hereford x Friesian		Blue Grey	
	kg	lb	kg	lb
Autumn-Born Calf				
Calf rearing	0.6	1.3	0.7	1.5
First grazing season	0.7	1.5	0.6	1.3
Second winter housing				
Pre-mating	0.6	1.3	0.5	1.1
Post-mating	0.5	1.1	0.4	0.9
Second grazing season	0.7	1.5	0.6	1.3
OVERALL	0.6	1.3	0.55	1.2
Spring-Born Calf				
First grazing season	0.5	1.1	0.7	1.5
Second winter housing	0.6	1.3	0.4	0.9
Second grazing season	0.8	1.8	0.7	1.5
Third winter housing	0.6	1.3	0.6	1.3
OVERALL	0.6	1.3	0.55	1.2

TABLE 8.11

Land Requirements for Replacements at Various Calving Ages

Hectares/Acres per Livestock Unit		Hectares/Acres Required to Calving Age					
		2 Years		2½ Years		3 Years	
Ha	Acres	Ha	Acres	Ha	Acres	Ha	Acres
0.4	1.0	0.4	1.0	0.55	1.4	0.7	1.75
0.5	1.25	0.5	1.25	0.75	2.0	1.0	2.5
0.7	1.75	0.7	1.75	1.0	2.5	1.3	3.25

(After M.A.F.F. Booklet 2422, 1983c)

References

MEAT AND LIVESTOCK COMMISSION/MILK MARKETING BOARD (1976) Rearing Replacements for Beef and Dairy Herds. pp. 1-56.

MINISTRY OF AGRICULTURE, FISHERIES AND FOOD (1983c) Rearing Spring-Born Friesian Dairy Heifers to Calve at 2½ Years. Booklet 2422. MAFF, Alnwick. pp. 1-23.

REARING REPLACEMENT BULLS

Dairy Bulls

Many dairy bulls are weaned from their dams but are allowed to suck a nurse cow - usually an old cow of good nature or one with only three quarters, or other problems. Often the cow will suckle several calves. Other calves will be fed milk substitute and although many will be early-weaned, at about five or six weeks old, some will receive restricted milk for up to 12 weeks. Good quality hay and highly palatable concentrate are usually made available from an early age. At the appropriate time the bulls will usually graze but their feeding will be supplemented with concentrates, often at a level of 2 - 4 kg (4.4 - 9.0 lb) per day. The cattle will usually receive the best grazing and will be transferred after weaning to a silage or hay aftermath in mid-July. The cattle will be yarded in the early autumn and will continue to be fed good quality roughage (hay or silage) and concentrates. The time of sale of the bulls will vary but most change hands for the first time between one and two years old. During the rearing period the aim is to ensure that the animals grow steadily and strongly without putting on fat.

Beef Bulls

Most beef bulls, whether autumn or spring-born, will remain on their dam until 5 to 10 months old. In some beef breeds or where the dam does not produce much milk the bull may subsequently be transferred to a nurse cow. The cow may be of the same breed but it is more likely to be of dairy or dairy cross origin. While at grass and sucking, the bull will have access to creep containing good quality concentrates and possibly also roughage. Following weaning, if the animal is still at grass, he will continue to receive concentrates and other forage.

In the autumn the animal may be yarded in a small group with other bulls or kept in a single pen. When the latter occurs, it is always advisable to ensure that the animal is within sight and sound of other animals. Concentrates are again usually fed and the bull will probably be broken in to the halter if this has not been done previously. The animal tends to be given good quality feed while housed or at yarding until it is sold. The age of sale of the animals again varies considerably according to when born, the timing of pedigree bull sales, as well as current fashions. Most tend to be sold between one and two years old. The aim is to grow the cattle so that they are strong and healthy but without too great a covering of fat. A few years ago many bulls at pedigree sales were sold at about a year old, but at present the majority are probably sold at 1½ years old or greater.

Advantages

1. A good bull with correct breeding and conformation is more valuable than any other type of animal of his breed. High prices tend to be paid for animals going for export or they are paid by other breeders requiring particular blood lines or when the bulls are to be used for artificial insemination.

2. Such a system creates great interest for both stockmen and owner.

3. The name and characteristics of a good bull will enhance the name of the parent herd and subsequently increase the reputation and value of progeny from the herd.

Disadvantages

1. Many pedigree animals which are not looked on favourably by customers will make little more than beef steers of the same weight and do not repay the extra inputs given to the animals.

2. The animals are kept a long time before there is a return on capital.

3. Although the breeding programme can be controlled, it is often a long time before the characteristics of the bull can be ascertained. This means much money will have been invested in bulls which are not of sufficient quality.

4. There is a considerable demand on labour in ensuring adequate individual attention to feeding, handling, etc.

5. Costs of feed tend to be high.

Veterinary Problems

Usually calves are well looked after so problems tend to be few.

1. Enzootic pneumonia.
2. Ringworm.
3. Pediculosis.

Rearing Animals

1. Scrotal or inguinal herniae. These are often not seen until the animal is over six months old.
2. Umbilical hernia. As these occur just anterior to the prepuce they are often missed unless a thorough examination of the area is made.
3. Pasteurellosis on housing.
4. Parasitic gastroenteritis.
5. Parasitic bronchitis (husk).

REFERENCES

ALLEN, D and KILKENNY, B (1984) Planned Beef Production. 2nd Edition. Granada Technical Books, London. pp. 1;229.

COMBEN, N (1984) Toxicity of the ionophores. Veterinary Record 114, 128.

DEEBLE, F K (1981) Principles of genetic improvement. British Cattle Veterinary Association Proceedings for 1980;1981. British Cattle Veterinary Association, Macclesfield. pp. 99-104.

MEAT AND LIVESTOCK COMMISSION (1974) Dairy-Bred Calves using Cereals and Arable Products. Beef Production Handbook No. 2, Meat and Livestock Commission, Bletchley. pp. 1-60.

MEAT AND LIVESTOCK COMMISSION (1976) Cattle Facts. A Manual of Economic Standards. Meat and Livestock Commission, Bletchley. pp. 1-132.

MEAT AND LIVESTOCK COMMISSION (1977) Data Sheets. Meat and Livestock Commission, Bletchley. pp. 1-72.

MEAT AND LIVESTOCK COMMISSION (1978) Grazing Management. Beef Production Handbook No. 4. Meat and Livestock Commission, Bletchley. pp. 1-44.

MEAT AND LIVESTOCK COMMISSION (1979) U.K. Meat and Livestock Statistics. Meat and Livestock Commission, Bletchley.

MEAT AND LIVESTOCK COMMISSION (1983) Beef Yearbook. Meat and Livestock Commission, Bletchley. pp. 1-106.

MEAT AND LIVESTOCK COMMISSION/MILK MARKETING BOARD (1976) Rearing Replacements for Beef and Dairy Herds. Meat and Livestock Commission, Bletchley. pp. 1-56.

MINISTRY OF AGRICULTURE, FISHERIES AND FOOD (1977) Straw as a Feeding Stuff. Leaflet 551, M.A.F.F., Pinner. pp. 1-7.

MINISTRY OF AGRICULTURE, FISHERIES AND FOOD (1982a) Grass Silage: Quality and Feeding. Leaflet 494, M.A.F.F., Alnwick. pp. 1-11.

MINISTRY OF AGRICULTURE, FISHERIES AND FOOD (1982b) Grazing Management for Beef Cattle. Grassland Practice No. 11. Booklet 2051. M.A.F.F., Alnwick. pp. 1-16.

MINISTRY OF AGRICULTURE, FISHERIES AND FOOD (1983a) Agricultural Statistics. Press Notice No. 236. M.A.F.F., London.

MINISTRY OF AGRICULTURE, FISHERIES AND FOOD (1983b) Silage Effluent. Waste Management Booklet 2429. M.A.F.F., Alnwick. pp. 1-10.

MINISTRY OF AGRICULTURE, FISHERIES AND FOOD (1983c) Rearing Spring-Born Friesian Dairy Heifers to Calve at 2½ Years. Booklet 2422. M.A.F.F., Alnwick. pp. 1-23.

MINISTRY OF AGRICULTURE, FISHERIES AND FOOD/DEPARTMENT OF AGRICULTURE AND FISHERIES FOR SCOTLAND/WELSH OFFICE AGRICULTURAL DEPARTMENT (1983) Codes of Recommendations for the Welfare of Livestock. Cattle. Leaflet 701. M.A.F.F., Alnwick. pp. 1-16.

PAIN, B F and BROOM, O M (1978) The effects of injected and surface spread slurry on the intake and grazing behaviour of dairy cows. Animal Production 26, 75-83.

ROBERTSON, I S, WILSON, J C and FRASER, H M (1979) Immunological castration in male cattle. Veterinary Record 105, 556-557.

ROBERTSON, I S, WILSON, J C, ROWLAND, A C and FRASER, H M (1981) Further studies on immunological castration in male cattle. Veterinary Record 108, 381-382.

SOUTHGATE, J (1982) The Friesian contribution to British beef. British Friesian Journal 64, No. 3, May 1982, 218-219.

INDEX

Note: Major entries to the subject are underlined.

Note: Major entries to the subject are underlined.